THE INCAS

PEOPLE OF THE SUN

BY THE SAME AUTHOR

The Sun Kingdom of the Aztecs

Maya. Land of the Turkey and the Deer

THE INCAS

PEOPLE OF THE SUN

by

VICTOR W. VON HAGEN

Illustrated by Alberto Beltrán

THE WORLD PUBLISHING COMPANY
NEW YORK

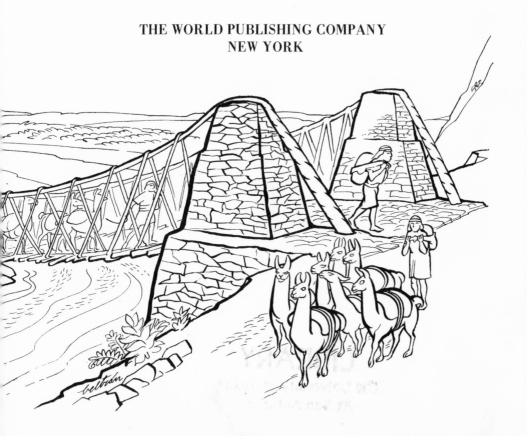

For the two,

who were born in the Land of the Sun

Adriana   Bettina

von Hagen

Published by The World Publishing Company
110 East 59th Street, New York, New York 10022

Published simultaneously in Canada by
Nelson, Foster & Scott Ltd.

Library of Congress Catalog Card Number: 61-12014
Second Printing July 1971

CONTENTS

Pronunciations for unfamiliar words

are given in the Index

THE CHASQUI-RUNNER

THEY were just hanging the suspension bridge when the runner arrived. *Chasqui*-runners were always arriving and departing, since they were the messengers of the empire, so there should have been nothing unusual about this particular runner. Still, there was. Men stopped their work to gather about him. Yet only for a moment; then they were called back to work.

For finishing the bridge at Cajas was vital. It was an important link on the Inca highway. It was, to be sure, a small bridge and only one of the hundreds on the great road that bound the Inca Empire together. Still, a fallen bridge was a missing link in a chain; it could bring travel to a halt. Troops moved over it on their way to battle, and over it went people traveling to the weekly fairs. Daily, hundreds of llamas—white, black, and brown—traveled it in their stately way, carrying the trade goods

7

of empire. So for fifteen days the people of Cajas had been working to repair the bridge.

The trouble had started with a thunderstorm, and for weeks afterward, or so it seemed, rain had fallen in torrents. It was really more rain than the priests had asked for. They had offered prayers to the Thunder God to send them the withheld promise of rain so that the planted fields would be watered. But even gods should be moderate; it had rained day after day. And the days were so darkened by storms that they seemed only a thin solution of the night. Little rills trickling through the grass of the high country suddenly became brooks; brooks which flowed lazily within banks shaded by *molle* trees suddenly became rivers; and the rivers turned into brawling streams of water. The river which ran through Cajas raged for days at its confining banks, and so in time the water had torn down the foundation of the suspension bridge. The day the bridge fell, Huamán, son of Mayta, was working in the fields. The rain had at long last gone its wetting way, and the Indians of Cajas had returned to their work. It was Huamán's chore to chase away the birds and the deer who were eating the half-ripened corn. He sat in the field, his head covered with a fox's pelt, and whirled stones from his sling at anything that dared to nibble at the corn.

Huamán was one of those who made up the Inca Empire, and already he was a farmer like all other people who lived by the soil. As a boy of twelve, halfway between child and man, he both played and worked. Naturally bronze-colored, he was slightly built, with small wrists and large hands (because he used them a great deal). Like others who live at high altitudes, his chest was somewhat large; one develops larger lungs in the rare air of great heights. His legs were strong, because ever since he had learned to walk, he had been carrying loads and climbing.

Although llamas might be ridden for fun, they were chiefly pack animals and everything had to be carried on their backs. When Huamán was four he had been given a small basket which was slung over his back and held to his forehead by a tumpline. Each year his father increased the load Huamán carried in it. Mayta could carry seventy-five pounds on his back in this way, with the weight suspended from his forehead, and move at a slow trot for many hours a day. Huamán was now able to carry half that weight.

The thing that all people noticed about Huamán when they noticed him at all were his eyes. Into his round bronze face, nature had placed large, brown almond-shaped eyes. They were even more arresting than his hooked nose and high cheekbones. His eyes, in fact, were the first thing his parents had noticed when he opened them for the first time. They were bright and very alert, like those of a hawk. So they had called him Huamán, meaning "hawk."

Huamán dressed like most men in an *onka*, a loose garment made of a long single piece of wool cloth with a hole in the center of it for his head. The *onka* had no sleeves. Under this he wore a breechclout, a cloth which wrapped around his waist in back and in front. He had, in fact, just received the *wara cicoy*, or breechclout. Like others when they reached the age of twelve, Huamán had been given it at a very solemn ceremony. It was a symbol that he had become almost a man. Naturally, he was very proud of it.

He also owned a *chumpi*-belt to hold his tunic in place, a brilliant red-and-blue one decorated with hawks' heads and flowers, which his mother had woven for him. He also wore a woolen cloak when it was cold. So this, with a woolen slingshot, which he wrapped around his long black hair when not in use, made up almost all of Huamán's worldly goods. The exception was his sandals, which were of deer hide.

Huamán's hawklike eyes had been the first to see the bridge lying in the water. Not that it would have been difficult to see. It was a suspension bridge, the floor of it supported by two rope cables as thick as Huamán's body. The raging river beneath it had washed away the banks that held the masonry, and the rope cables had fallen. Huamán had run to the village to tell his father, who was the official in charge of the bridge at Cajas and of that section of the Inca road. He had known he would find Mayta in the plaza.

The village of Cajas was very old. No one knew how old. It had been old even before the Incas conquered it eighty years ago. The people of Cajas were an important tribe whose head village was at Huancapampa, a few miles away. There were

many other such tribes in the vast Andes. Each tribe spoke a different language; each had different customs; each wore different dress, and their gods went by different names. And in olden times, they had warred with each other constantly. The one thing they had had in common was that each tribe planted and harvested the same type of crops.

Then the Inca people had come. They were Andean Indians who spoke a language known as Quechua; and some even called them by that name. At first, they referred to themselves as *Capaccuna,* only using the name *Inca* to designate their ruler. So the Incas had come as a conquering army, and by 1450 all the northern tribes were made part of the Inca Empire. Roads ran the full length of the land, and now there was Inca justice, Inca

religion, and taxes for all. The people were made to speak
Quechua, the Inca language.

Cajas had long since been a part of the Inca Empire. In its
center was the plaza, at one end of which stood the Sun Temple.
It was a pyramid faced with stone and had stone steps leading
to the top. At its summit was the temple. About the plaza were
other stone buildings, including a house for the Inca, the royal
tampu, where he stopped when traveling. Though it was of a
severe style, it was a beautiful building made of stones joined
artfully together without cement. The steeply inclined roof was
thatched with grass. Behind the buildings and out from the plaza
spread the houses of the people.

When Huamán reached the village, he had found his father
at work in front of the royal storage houses from which corn was
being taken and put into brown woolen bags. An accountant
was standing near-by, registering each bag on his knot-string
recorder as it was filled. Mayta was easily recognizable, for across
his face was a long scar he had received in battle. Like all the
others, he wore the *onka,* held together by a woolen belt.
Wrapped about his head was his sling, and in it was a copper
ornament shaped like a half wheel. This was his badge of office,
for he was a *pachaca curaca,* an official over one hundred men.

When Mayta heard about the bridge, he had gone at once to
the keeper of the records to send a message. This old man wore
in his headdress a silver crescent moon, signifying that he was
a *quipu-camayoc,* a keeper of the *quipus*—the knot-string records
—and a reader of them.

The Incas had no writing. Instead, they used a *quipu* to record
things and help them remember. *Quipu* meant "knot"; it had
one long main cord and from it hung strings which were tied
into half-hitch knots. Each knot represented decimal units, from
ten to one hundred. Some *quipus* had strings of different colors,

representing diverse concepts and objects, as black for war, white
for alpacas, yellow for gold. The *quipu* could record numbers of
things, also the dates when important things had occurred. As
Mayta talked, the keeper of the *quipus* tied knots into the strings.
Each of these knots referred to numbers, and each string referred
to a different thing. The *chasqui* who was to carry the message
would remember which strings referred to llamas, which to food,
which to men, which to bridges.

With these facts in mind, the *chasqui* quickly ran off along the
road to the next post. Within a mile and a half he would meet
another *chasqui* waiting for messages to whom he would repeat
the contents of the message and hand over the *quipu*. The new
chasqui would then run full speed to the next post. So it went
from post to post. *Chasquis* ran night and day and were able

to relay a message from Quito to Cusco, a distance of 1,250 miles, in five days.

Mayta's message was as follows: Tell the Governor that the Cajas bridge has fallen and that I, Mayta, am putting one hundred llamas and two hundred men to work, and that it will take fifteen days to repair it.

Meanwhile, the people from Cajas were called away from whatever they were doing to work on the bridge. Huamán was put to work with many other boys and younger men to gather fibers from the *cabuya*. At an altitude of over 9,000 feet the higher *pampa*, or plain, is covered with grass, and trees are small and scarce. The Indians depended on the *cabuya*, a plant with wide leaf-pads rimmed with long sharp spines. The width of each leaf is more than two outstretched palms, and it is about five feet long. Each *cabuya* has fifteen or more such pads, and in the center of them grows a stalk which when it flowers is more than fifteen feet tall. In the summertime it bears beautiful golden-brown blossoms.

Cabuya was easy to cut; Huamán had only to bend over, swing at the base of a pad with his sharp bronze *tumi*-knife, and it would fall off. As soft as it was, it had strong fibers within. When dried beneath the hot Andean sun and the soft pith removed, it was reduced to long, tough brown fibers. It was from these that rope was made.

From the hill overlooking Cajas, Huamán could see everyone working. Below, men were pulling the *cabuya* fibers through the teeth of an upright bronze comb. This action took away the last of the green pulp and left only the fibers. When these were washed, others twisted them into strings. The string was then plaited into rope as thick as a finger; and, in turn, strands of these were made into rope cables.

People worked together. They did everything together. The

fields were tilled, houses built, roads were made—together. It was this communal activity that made the Inca Empire. No one resented work. Work was thought by each to be an end in itself. But work had to be a ceremonial, or else it lacked meaning. So when they worked they sang. Men plaiting eight large rope cables into one immense cable as thick as a man's body, were singing now. The song, a victory song, drifted up to where Huamán stood:

> "Victory Ho, Victory Ho,
> Here twisting the rope,
> > here the *cabuya,*
> Here the sweat,
> > here the toil."

And from another place where others worked came an answering chorus:

"Work, men, work!"

The Cajas bridge was not large. It was not more than fifty feet long, yet like hundreds of others it kept the empire together. It was "a little brother of the road," and Inca roads were thousands of miles long, reaching from one end of the great empire to the other. Few except the Inca, his imperial governors, and his generals had ever seen the whole of the realm. It was so large that a person like Huamán could not even grasp how large it really was.

The Inca Empire included three vast regions: the Andes, a fringe of rain-filled jungles, and the hot desert coast. The jungles lay to the east, a vast ocean of trees through which enormous rivers wound their way. In these humid, hot lands lived Indians in large tribal villages. Rising abruptly out of the jungles and towering over them were the Andes. This great range, running through what is now Peru, was warm at midday and freezing at night. Rain fell in seasons, and the people built their houses of stone. Most of the empire's population lived in these high altitudes. The last region was the hot desert coast west of the Andes. Rain seldom fell on its sands; it was nothing but desert for two thousand miles except where rivers from the mountains made oases.

The empire began, they said, in the north beyond Quito at the Rumi-chaca bridge and stretched south for 3,250 miles. All along the way roads were marked with *topos,* stone distance-markers four and one half miles apart. The main road was twenty-four feet wide and built with a stone parapet on either side. It went all the way down to Chile. There it stopped at the edge of a river, and a stone fortress marked its end and the end of the Inca Empire. Beyond that were the wild and ferocious Araucano Indians, who walked swathed in furs about their wind-swept lands.

All along the road were cities and towns, called *marcas*. Some were very large, having as many as fifty thousand people; others were only villages. The road climbed so high at times that it lay close to the regions of eternal snow, that is, above sixteen thousand feet. At other times the road dipped down into dry valleys where the air was as hot as the desert. But no matter where the road went—and it went, it seemed, everywhere—there were always *tampus,* or resthouses, for travelers. Every four *topos,* or eighteen miles (as far as a man could walk in a day), there was such a resthouse. It was the duty of the Indians living nearest to it to see that there was wood for fire and corn, potatoes, and dried meat for the traveler at the *tampu.* The Inca himself had royal *tampus* which only he or his entourage could use.

The roads helped hold the empire together. Five million Indians were ruled from Cusco. This Cusco was their capital,

the heart of the great empire. From out of its very center went the roads that ran into the surrounding territory. Laws were made which covered all facets of their lives; everything was arranged for them. They were told when to plant, when to harvest their crops, when to play, when to weep. There were rules for mothers; there were rules for children. If they did not marry at the age they were supposed to, the Inca made them marry; if a man had no girl in prospect, the Inca's governors found one for him.

The one rule followed by all was this: *Ama sua, ama llulla, ama cheklla.* Do not steal, do not lie, do not be lazy.

The people feared their Inca, but they also worshiped him. To them he was divine; he was the son of the Sun. When he died, the Inca would say that his father, the Sun God, had called him. The Lord-Inca constantly visited his lands, wanting to see with his own eyes that his laws were carried out. His concern was for his people because his power came from the people. So he had many names: the Only Inca; the Son of the Sun; the Lover of the Poor. Huamán had once seen the Lord-Inca passing through Cajas, carried in a litter by eight men. The boy had fallen on his knees as had all the others; one dared not even look at the Inca directly. Huamán's father said that even the greatest lords of the land trembled when they came before him. They had to come before him barefoot, carrying on their backs some sort of burden to show him their humility. Yet the Inca thought of his people. He made laws not so that the people would fear him, but in order to make life better for ordinary people.

On the fifteenth day the giant rope cables were ready. They were a foot thick and sixty feet long. More than one hundred Indians were needed to carry one cable. In the meantime, masons had replaced the stone pillars which would hold the suspension cables.

Now men on a crude raft paddled across the river carrying guide ropes attached to the cables in their hands. On the other side, other Indians pulled on the guide ropes until the rope cables were at the edge of the river where they were placed over the tops of high wooden platforms built for that purpose. Then, slowly, the ropes were pulled across the fifty-foot width of the river, stretched across high stone towers built on either side, and made as taut as possible. These cables were the suspensions from which the bridge would hang. The ends were tied to tree trunks at the entrance to the bridge, buried deep in the earth and secured by rocks piled on top of them.

Indians now scurried across the cable suspensions like monkeys crawling upside down along a branch of a tree. At intervals they tied other ropes which soon formed a skein of ropes like a hammock. On this the wooden floor boards of the bridge were laid. Such a bridge could hold numerous men and llamas passing over it at a single moment.

It was just at this moment that the *chasqui*-runner arrived. The runner said that he was the last of a relay of *chasquis* carrying a message from the coast. They were trained from childhood to run quickly even at high altitudes. *Chasquis* wore a special headdress—bird plumes around a crown of plaited fibers, the plumes fluttering behind them as they ran. They also carried a shell horn to make known their coming from some distance away. By law no one was allowed to stay the *chasqui* in his flight, and no one was allowed to ask him what message he carried except the one to whom the message was directed.

Yet this particular message could not be kept secret. "Out of the sea, out of the *hatun-cocha,* have come men who look like

Viracochas. They have white faces and wear heavy dark beards."

The *curaca,* the chief of Tumpiz (now Tumbes), on the sea-coast at the northern end of the empire, had sent the messenger. When the *quipu-camayoc*—the reader of the records—came up to him, the runner handed the record over to him.

No one knew what to say when the message was given. Viracocha, the Creator God, had disappeared into the sea many centuries ago and he had said that he would one day return. Could this be . . . ?

The message had to go on at that very instant to the Inca, who was in the north at Tumipampa. The old man in charge of the *quipus* tied more knots into the strings and was preparing to send another *chasqui* off on the relay when the sound of horns caused him to pause.

Warriors dressed for battle, shield in hand and lances held high, suddenly appeared from the direction of the river. They announced that Quisquis, the General, was approaching.

Quisquis! Everyone who had been a soldier knew that name, for he was the Inca's greatest general. Brave and fierce, he had led his army over all the empire, conquering here, punishing there. Next to the Inca, he was feared perhaps more than any other in the empire.

Quisquis arrived, carried in a litter consisting of two long poles onto which was built an overhead canopy. It was covered with beautifully woven cloth that had little pieces of gold and silver bangles tied into it. As to the poles, they were covered with gold plate. Each side of the litter was carried on the shoulders of eight men, strong rugged Rucanas Indians clad in blue. Behind them walked—or rather, trotted, for that was the walk of the Indian—a hundred more Rucanas to relieve the others when they tired.

Because he had fought the Inca wars so well Quisquis was one of the Big Ears. He belonged to the lower nobility and so was allowed to wear jeweled ear spools. His beautiful ear ornaments were of blue turquoise and white shell. On the white shell there were tiny golden lizards.

Quisquis wore a stern look, almost angry, made even more fierce by his red-and-black face paint. On his head was a conical wooden helmet, also painted red and black. His *onka* was woven from vicuña wool and had the look of brown silk. He sat erect on the small seat within the litter, holding his golden halberd lance.

In front of the litter and behind it, in an orderly fashion, were his soldiers. All wore helmets over knitted caps, and like their general, their faces were painted. They wore quilted-cotton armor over their sleeveless tunics. Each tunic was different in color and pattern. Only the shields, which everyone carried, were the same. For each *ayllu,* or earth-community, had its own device. All who were of one company carried the same shield. The men were also armed with a lance and axes with stone heads or one of bronze with six pointed stars. Each man wore a cloth sling wrapped around the crown of his head in such a way that the ends hung down alongside his long black hair.

Having been summoned by the Inca, Quisquis was on his way to Tumipampa. He had been carried most of the eight hundred miles from Cusco. In the plaza at Cajas, he learned the news from the coast. The *chasqui* and the knot-string reader came forward, and the message was repeated. A strange ship with large sails had landed at Tumpiz. There were thirty men aboard. All had white skins and black beards except one, who was black all over. One who came ashore had a helmet that seemed to be silver and a tunic of metal. He carried a thick stick which sounded like thunder and belched fire when it went off. Whatever came out of it could shatter a drinking mug fifty paces distant. The chief of Tumpiz thought that these strangers might be returning Viracochas.

The *chasqui* was then ordered to start the relay of the message to Cusco to the south and to Tumipampa in the north. With that, Quisquis, with trumpets blowing, took his departure.

The people bowed low until he had disappeared over the Inca road. It was only then that young Huamán said aloud that which most were thinking:

"Viracocha, Viracocha, why has he returned?"

VIRACOCHA,
THE CREATOR GOD

THE HOUSE of Huamán's family, their *wasi* as they called it, was much like all the others. It was a large rectangular room built of fieldstones set into mud. The outside was then plastered with more mud to which was added grass that had been churned by their feet. The roof was pitched so that it would shed the rain and was made by tying gnarled branches together. Then it was thickly and beautifully thatched with gray-green *ichu* grass. Their house and the houses of five other families, all related to Mayta's family, formed a sort of square. It was a common yard, or *cancha*. In this yard the families dried their maize and froze potatoes into *chuñu*. Here wandered wild ducks and a dog native to the Andes. It was small and seldom ever used for hunting; it was mute and did not bark. Some other tribes even ate dog flesh, but the Incas had scorn for such people, calling them Dog-eaters.

23

In addition to dogs and ducks, the Indians kept as pets the wild *wachwa*, a white-gray snow goose, whose home was in the region of perpetual snow. When young, they were as tame as dogs. In the *cancha* the Indians sun-dried their llama meat. Cut into long thin strips, it was known as *charqui*.

The house had been built with the aid of other people of the *ayllu,* the basic social unit of the land. Everyone belonged to one. Huamán was born into one; he would die in it. All worked together. All helped one another. The *ayllu* owned the land; it also owned the llama herds. No individual owned land. People were allowed the use of the land to grow crops on it, but they could not sell the land because it belonged to the community. Even the Inca, exalted as he was, belonged to such a community; it was a royal one but an *ayllu* just the same.

The Indians belonging to a given society believed themselves to be of the same kin. So it was a cell, a social cell. The whole Inca Empire was made up of hundreds of such social cells, some large, some small. Each elected a leader who was called a *mallcu.* And he was aided by a council, usually old men who had seen life and knew something of its problems.

The structure of Inca society was pyramidal, like a Sun Temple. The broad base was the able-bodied worker. He was called a *puric.* Ten *purics* were controlled by a straw boss, and ten of these straw bosses had a foreman (Mayta, being in charge of one hundred men as the caretaker of the Inca road at Cajas, was such a foreman).

Ten foremen had, in turn, a supervisor who was thus the leader of a thousand men. Ten of these chieftains were lorded over by a *hono-curaca,* who was the chieftain of ten thousand men, and finally, there was an imperial governor of each district, the *apo,* who was always a relative of the Inca. At the very summit of the social pyramid was the Inca himself. He was god or almost god; his mere word could order death.

The house of Huamán was not as bare inside as his cousins who lived in the hot coastland said it was. They teased him, saying that he lived like a bear in a cave, but it was really not that. It is true, the house had no door. Then, houses did not have doors; a beautiful woolen tapestry, called *kumpi,* took the place of a door. Nor were there any windows. At an altitude of over 9,000 feet it was too cold, and in any case Incas had no glass for windows. On the hard mud-packed floors were woven rush mats. Over these, when they had them, they laid llama-skin rugs or sometimes the hide of a hairy tapir or pelts of mountain fox or deer. In niches in the wall were clay images of their gods.

A corner of the house served as kitchen. The hearth was made of stones sunk into the floor. On the wall hung wooden cooking spoons, and wooden pegs held cooking pots that were not in use on the hearth. There was no chimney; the smoke from the kitchen fire blackened the walls and the thatch roof and found its own way out. In a darker corner, scampering about, were *cuis,* the furry animals, smaller than rabbits, which we call guinea pigs. These rodents are charming little animals, brown and white, black or gray. The Indians, at a time lost in antiquity, had tamed them as they tamed the llama. They called them *cui* because of the sound they made. It was the first sound Huamán remembered from the time he was born into this cold Andean world. The *cui* had new ones born continuously; it was the Indians' main source of meat.

At the other end of the house, sometimes separated from the main room by a tapestry, were the sleeping quarters. The Indians had no beds other than a llama skin or a rush mat; their bed covering consisted of the woolen cloaks, the *yacolla,* which

they draped about themselves during the day. The Inca himself had no better bed. In the corner was a large wickerwork basket finely woven of rush; this held their festive clothes. Here, too, they kept their golden ornaments, necklaces, and the other small, intimate things of their lives. Deer antlers on the wall served as hooks on which to hang extra clothing. Ropes made of llama hides, slingshots, spears, clubs, and wooden *macanas*—swords made of large *chonta*-wood into which sharpened *tumi*-knives were set—also hung there.

All these were on hand because the Indian was both farmer and soldier. Everyone able to be one was a soldier. Their shields identified them. The totem device of Huamán's community was the head of a bear, the *ucumari,* a small black bear with wide circles around its eyes. A shield with this device was carried by all the warriors of Cajas. It symbolized their home, their earth. No matter where they went—and as warriors some Indians traveled great distances—they always remembered the spot of earth where they belonged.

When twilight closed in upon them, which it did at six o'clock, it was suddenly dark. Indian families had no light, no oil lamps, only the light of the fire and the bright glow from pottery braziers which were placed about the room to snuff out the cold. There in the evening sat Mayta, the father; his wife, whom the children called Mama; Huamán, the eldest, and his three sisters, one of whom was a baby. Just as his mother had sung to him, so she now sang to her newly born:

Caylla llapi	In this place
Punuñqui	You will sleep
Punuñqui	You will sleep
Chaupi tuta	And at midnight
Hámusac	I will come
Hámusac	I will come
Hámusac	I will come

Indians ate only two meals a day: at nine in the morning and at five in the afternoon. They rose early, before the sun. As soon as they roused the fire by blowing on the coals and putting small pieces of wood on it, they drank *aca* (now known as *chicha*), a beverage made from corn. Then they went out to work in their fields, returning at nine to eat their first meal. If the fields were far away, they carried their food with them. Food was either boiled or roasted, and the second meal was not much different from the first. Mostly it consisted of a soup or stew. There was also hominy, maize soaked in lime to make it swell and soften the grain. When washed and boiled with herbs and sharp, hot chili peppers it tasted savory. This was called *motepatasca*. Maize bread was made by braising boiled corn on a flat stone and forming a dough of it; then it was baked in the ashes. Maize was also toasted in open dishes. Popcorn made from a special type of maize was very welcome and considered a delicacy.

Stews, called *locro,* were based on dried llama meat, deer, cui, or duck. To this was added potatoes and vegetables (which were scarce), then chili peppers for flavoring and *chuñu* as a thickening agent.

In order to make *chuñu,* the women had to put potatoes in high places where they would freeze during the night. In the daytime when they thawed, the women squashed out the water with their feet. Alternately frozen and unfrozen, in a few weeks the potatoes were turned into a dry, white potato flour, and this was *chuñu.* If stored in a dry place, it would last for many years.

A dish liked by everyone was *chupe.* It was made from freshwater shrimps, which the people at Cajas could get from the coastal people, two days' walk away. The shrimps were boiled to make a broth; then the meat was taken out of the shell and mixed with the broth, thickened with *chuñu,* potatoes, *molle-*pepper, and chili.

Mealtime was a serious time, serious because it took so much work for the Indian to get his food. The men sat on rush mats, facing the big bowl of stew. Women and girls served the food with a big wooden spoon, then sat apart and ate alone. Each member of the family had his own eating dish. In Huamán's case they had been made by his father and decorated by his mother. One had birds painted on it in bright reds and yellows; another showed women holding cups of *aca*-beer. Others were decorated with flowers. No one ever put salt directly into his food. Instead, each had his own piece of rock salt which he licked from time to time.

Salt was scarce. It had to be brought from the coast, and grain-eaters like the Incas needed it very much. Some Indians developed large growths on their necks (goiters) because they lacked iodine in their diet. For this reason the Inca told them they must eat *chaquill,* or seaweed, a rich source of iodine. Thus many stews were prepared with *chaquill.* Seaweed was so important that one of the roads into Cusco (the one that came directly from the coast) bore the name of Chaquill-chaca, "the seaweed bridge."

At night when the second meal was finished, people busied themselves with other necessities of daily living. Women spun fibers of wool into thread for their weaving. In fact, women spun whenever they had a leisure moment. With a wooden distaff placed under the arm and a wad of wool tied to its end, they spun as they walked. Their left hand pulled down the fiber, the right hand whirled the spindle stick, and the thread was formed. When they could get it by trade, the women also spun cotton. This came from the hot coast or from the even hotter *yungas*-jungles. Then the threads, whether wool or cotton, were dyed. Men gathered color-bearing minerals for the reds and greens; black they got from wood or from the pith of a seed called

genipa; carmine came from the bright red seeds of a plant burr called *achiote.* Purple was taken from sea shells.

Once the threads were dyed, weaving began. Every woman learned to weave as a child. Mainly they used the backstrap loom, called so because a strap around the back of the weaver pulled the loom and thus the warp threads tight. In Huamán's house there were many such looms attached to the wall, each with half-finished cloth. His sister Curi was already a weaver. Women wove all the garments, as well as body armor for warriors, tapestries for the walls, and *chumpi*-belts to hold tunics together. They supplied the empire with cloth. All of the Inca's clothes were woven by the Sun Maidens, and he never wore the same clothes twice (they had to be burned, for they were too sacred for anyone else to wear). So women had to weave constantly.

Men worked at night on other things. Since they were farmers, maize and potatoes were *their* food and were watched carefully. Ears of *sara* (maize) were gone over to select the most unusual kernels for seedlings. They were put into a bin called *Sara-mama* (maize mother). When they were not repairing their digging tools, they were making new weapons. Some men wove rush mats, others worked in metal—bronze, copper, silver or gold. Some carved bowls out of stone; others modeled llamas out of copper; some beat out *tupu* pins of thin copper, which women used to hold their shawls together.

Night was also the time for storytelling. The Incas had no writing. The old *quipu-camayoc* said he did not believe they had ever had it. That is why they had to develop their memories so well. When some great and stirring event occurred, official rememberers put it down in their minds. They would sing and chant it on all occasions. If, for example, they forgot a date or how many men were in a battle, they consulted the *quipu*.

At Cajas the *quipu-camayoc's* name was Ayri, which meant "battle-ax." No one knew how he had got this name. Whether it was because his sharp face looked like a battle-ax, or whether he was as sharp-edged as a battle-ax, no one knew. He was now very old and because he was so old he was allowed to chew the coca leaf.

Coca, which the Incas called the divine leaf, grew as a high bush in the *yungas,* the moist, hot lands east of the mountains. When it was chewed, the leaf yielded cocaine and gave relief from cold and hunger. Not everyone was allowed to use it; only the very old, the priests, the witch doctors, and the Inca were allowed to chew coca.

Ayri sat in front of the brazier. He threw into it some handfuls of *taquia,* which is llama dung, and leaned back against the wall. From his coca-leaf pouch, a beautifully woven wool bag decorated with a line of red llamas marching across it, he drew out a handful of coca leaves. These he made into a wad which he put into his cheek. At that moment he looked less like a battle-ax and more like a chipmunk holding an outsize nut in his mouth. Out of the same bag Ayri took his lime stick, a small gourd with a long neck in which lime was kept. Lime was made from sea shells or from the ashes of the grain known as *quinoa.* The stick itself was a piece of bone which Ayri dipped into the gourd and licked. The lime would release the cocaine juices.

All day Huamán had been questioning himself about the *chasqui*-runner and his message. Now he wanted to know who these people were, these bearded men who had arrived. Why did the chief of Tumpiz think it was Viracocha? Ayri settled back against the wall, pulled his long, hooked nose and played with his ear lobes. They were without any ornaments and looked like the loose wattles of a turkey. But Ayri was now too old to care how he looked; he no longer wore his ear spools except when the Governor came, and then he had to.

"Who was Viracocha and why do we feel that these people are Viracochas? I will gladly tell you, and it behooves you to listen:

"Viracocha is the Creator God and is also known by a long name but mostly by the shorter one of Viracocha, the Creator God. He made the world of earth and sky and left it in darkness. Then he decided to make people to live in it, so he carved statues of stone in the shape of giants and gave them life. After a while,

when the giants displeased him, he destroyed them by turning some to stone and overwhelming the rest with a great flood from which there were only two survivors.

"Then he created a new race his own size to replace the giants that he had destroyed. First, he gave the world light by causing the sun and the moon to emerge from the island of Titicaca. The moon was originally brighter than the sun, but the sun was jealous and threw a handful of ashes in the moon's face, which paled her brilliance. Viracocha then modeled animals and men out of clay. He modeled each species of animal and tribe. On the models of men he painted the clothes they were to wear.

Then he gave men their customs, food, language, and songs and ordered them to descend to the earth to settle.

"Later Viracocha himself went to earth to see if the people were obeying his commands.

"Viracocha took the route of the Inca highway. Because he appeared only as an old man with a staff, many people along the way did not recognize him. At Cacha the people came out to stone him because they did not like strangers.

"Viracocha called down a fire from heaven which began to burn the rocks and so frightened the people that they begged him to forgive them. He took pity, and put out the fire with a blow of his staff. They built a shrine in his honor. Then Viracocha went to Cusco where he summoned the inhabitants to come out of a mountain. They honored him. He went northward from there toward Ecuador. Here, he said farewell to his people and set out across the Pacific, walking on water."

In 1525, two years ago, a white man had come to their realm. The old rememberer said that when the Inca's soldiers were attacked in the Gran Chaco, the jungles east of Bolivia, the troops were surprised that the one who led the jungle Indians was a white-skinned man with a black beard. When he was captured he spoke in a tongue no one knew. He escaped, but later, when he was killed, they saw that he had a completely white body. But all that had happened in the east. And now to the west, more white men with black beards had come, this time in a boat, sailing from out of the great sea—the *hatun-cocha*.

What did it mean? No one dared say until the old Inca Huayna Capac gave his answer.

CUSCO, THE FOUR QUARTERS
OF THE WORLD

THE WORLD is divided by four. And Cusco is the center of the
four divisions of the world. That is what every boy learned about
the Incas. That is what Huamán was learning now. He learned
how the Sun God sent down two of his children to create a new
race; one was Manco Capac and the other his sister Mama
Ocllo. They wandered along the Andes looking for the best
place to found a city and lay down their lineage. "Go," said the
Sun God, "and continue to go until you reach fertile land.
When the golden staff that I gave you can be thrown into the
earth so that it disappears, it will mean that the ground is fertile.
Stay there, build a city, start a family, make a nation!"

Manco Capac did as he was ordered. In the high mountains
he found a valley which lay at an altitude of 11,000 feet. On three
of its sides the mountains rose high and sheer. Many months

35

during the year these were snow-covered. On its southern side the valley opened up; two small rivers flowed through it and formed into one large river with fertile land on both sides.

Manco Capac and his sister called this place Cusco. There, they erected their first house, thatching it with straw. They named the house Curi-cancha, since the color of the straw resembled gold (*curi*). The date was 1150.

Every tribe has its myths, every nation its ideals; each tells a story of how its people came to be. The official story of the origin of the Incas was really very different from what was usually told. The Incas said that when they came to the earth, all of the other tribes were wild and lived like animals. It was the duty of the Incas to conquer them and civilize them. But many like Ayri, who had traveled much, knew that this was not wholly true. Before the Incas, there had been many other great tribes. The last to fall were the Chimús, and that was not quite seventy years ago. They ruled six hundred miles of coast, had a city as large as Cusco, and were very advanced. Before them had been the Mochicas; they were a great people one thousand years before the Incas arrived. And before them the Chavín, whose temple, an immense stone building with carved stone heads set in it, still survived. It was a shrine, and all agreed that it must be more than 2,500 years old.

Here in the high Andes there were also many great cities before the Incas arrived. Everyone talked of Tiahuanaco. It was a stone-built ceremonial center lying near Lake Titicaca. That lake, 12,500 feet high, was surrounded by snow-capped mountains. Yet its shoreline was fertile, and there were many people about it. They had lived there for a thousand years before the Incas came. Tiahuanaco had great stone buildings which Ayri himself had seen. There were huge gateways and stone steps. One, called the Gateway of Sun, was carved from a single piece of rock, thirty feet long.

All this meant that before the Incas arrived, there had been other great nations within the four quarters of the world.

Yet Cusco became the greatest. As time went its way, the Incas grew in power. First they developed their valley. Then they began to spread out into other valleys held by other tribes. There was war, constant war; but even in war the Incas also developed the land. When land was scarce they terraced it by laying down stone walls and filling them with earth. When more water was needed, they skillfully brought it down from high places in aqueducts. As they advanced they built roads. Four main roads came out of the great plaza of Cusco.

Cusco was called the Four Quarters of the World because the four roads which began in its center ran down to the four sections of the Inca Empire. Each quarter was known as a *suyu*. Cusco itself was known as Tawantin-suyu, the center of these four quarters. It was marvelous how Cusco was built, and someday Huamán would see it.

In the center of the city was the Joy Square. Here the great markets were held, here the dances, here the crowning of the new Inca. At one side was the Stone of War where all the generals took oath to the Inca. Around the great square were stone palaces of the ruling classes. Each time an Inca died, his mummy was placed inside his palace, and the new Inca built another for himself. The streets were narrow; buildings were one-storied, often two-storied. All the finer ones were built of stone, worked stones so beautifully fitted together that it was hard to know where one stone ended and the other began. The roofs were of

straw, just like those in Cajas, but real gold had been inserted
into some roofs so as to resemble straw. The goldsmiths made
long strands of gold that looked just like straw, and these were
placed in the thatch so that when the sun set, the whole roof
seemed to blaze with gold.

The rivers that flowed into the city were canalized; water, pure and clear, was brought down in ceramic pipes. There were baths and toilets for the people throughout the city.

Cusco was divided into two main sections. In Hurin, or Lower Cusco, lived the nobles; here were the Sun Temple, the House of the Virgins, and the Temple of the Snakes. In this part of Cusco was the Curi-cancha, the Golden Enclosure. It had changed much since the year 1150 when it was built by the first Inca, Manco Capac. The chief priest of the whole empire—the *Huillac Umu*—lived there now. The Golden Enclosure had six buildings within its high stone walls. There was a shrine to the Sun, one to the moon, one to the stars, the rainbow, and so on. The most famous part was the Inti-pampa, the Field of the Sun. In the center was a stone foundation encased in gold; on its sides was etched the image of the Sun. Its fields were not earth at all, but gold. The clods of earth were gold; the corn stalks were gold. The artisans had copied it exactly from nature. There were even life-sized llamas made of gold.

All metal belonged to the Inca, the gold and silver as well. Gold, he said, was the sweat of the Sun, silver the tears of the moon. All the metals taken from the mines had to be brought to Cusco, and the gold and silver taken from other tribes had to be deposited there, too. An entire section of the city was given over to the goldsmiths.

In addition to gold, the Incas had many other things of their empire deposited in Cusco. The royal storehouses were filled with corn, *chuñu,* and other foodstuffs. One was kept for sea-weed and sea food. Fresh fish was brought to Cusco by a relay of *chasquis* who ran the two hundred miles in two days. Cotton, white and silky, was stored here. There were also arsenals all over the city. Here the Incas deposited shields, lances, javelins, slings, swords, and even cotton armor—in case of war.

The other part of Cusco was Hanan, or Upper Cusco, where the common Indian lived. His house was like those in Cajas, fieldstone set in mud, plastered and painted. Here lived Indians from many parts of the empire; one could tell where they came from by their different headgear. Those from the *yungas,* the desert coast, went around muffled up to their noses because they were unused to the cold. Those from the shores of Lake Titicaca wore knitted caps that hung over the ears. The Cañaris from Cañar wore a sort of crown made of plaited rush. The Huancas had a broad, flat hat from which short ropes hung as far down as the lower jaw. The Inca had ordered that all his people must keep their own dress; in that way he would know where they came from.

The greatest thing in Cusco at which all marveled was the fortress, Sacsahuamán. It stood on a hill 600 feet above Cusco, overlooking the city. One of the great roads, the one that lead to the jungles, ran by it. It was so large that all of the 100,000 people of Cusco could have taken refuge in it. That was what it was for; it was a fortress, a *pucará*. When Cusco was attacked in 1438 the Incas had no such fort and they vowed they would never again be so defenseless.

Sacsahuamán was 1,500 feet long, built in three tiers, or sections. The lower stones weighed as much as seventy-five tons and were twenty-five feet high. These had been quarried with stone hammers and pried loose with bronze levers. Then each had been placed on hard wooden rollers, and by means of ropes, pulled to the fortress. Had Huamán any idea how great the work was? There must be more than 200,000 immense stones in the fortress: all had been pulled there by human power. There they were raised into place by ropes. While this was being done the stone masons chipped away until the joints of each rock fitted into the other. To put up the second layer of stones was even more difficult. The workmen had built an earth ramp sloping gently to the top of the lower stone. The huge stones for the second layer were pulled up the ramp and treated as the lower ones. They fitted into place on the lower stone so precisely that one could see only a thin line where the joints met.

It had taken eighty years to build Sacsahuamán, with twenty-five thousand Indians constantly at work on it. There was scarcely an Indian in the whole empire who had not spent some of his time working on it. It had, in fact, only recently been finished. If only the Inca Pachacuti could have lived to see it. . . .

Inca history was like this:

Almost two hundred years ago a great Indian named Roca was Lord-Inca. Cusco had grown far beyond its valley. The Incas pushed their empire south, then east into the warm, humid valleys. Between Cusco and the Pacific Ocean there was a rugged and mountainous area. The most direct route to the coast was through this region, but it was held by a fierce and sturdy tribe called Rucanas. They raised alpacas on the high prairies 14,000 feet above sea level. They were used to cold and hardships. It took many small wars until they later gave up; then the Inca honored them for their gallant fight. Passage to the west, to the Pacific and the sea was open to the Incas.

Now to the north there flowed the Apurimac River. It went through a canyon, at places a thousand feet deep. At first this stopped the Incas. The river was wide, swift, and treacherous; only a few weeks of the year was it low enough to get across by fording. The Inca sent out his engineers to scout the canyon walls, and at one place they found that the rock walls of the canyon were separated by only 140 feet.

The Lord-Inca said: "I will bridge the Apurimac."

He built a road by constructing a descending stairway—he called it a *pata-pata,* or step-road—which wound from the edge of the canyon to the place where the bridge would be erected. In 1350 the greatest suspension bridge in the whole empire was placed across the Apurimac. It was 148 feet long and rested or, better, swayed two hundred feet above the river. It seemed like a miracle to the people that a river which had defied man so long should have been conquered. And proudly the Lord-Inca was conveyed on a litter across the bridge. Once on the other side he said, "This shall be called Huaca-chaca, 'the holy bridge.'"

Many tribes were excited about this marvelous great bridge. Those called the Chancas, who lived across the Apurimac to the west, were even more so. They did not like the Incas. They feared them, and they wanted neither their Sun God nor their Inca. The Chancas wanted to keep their own gods. A fierce tribe of fighters and farmers, they had long believed that the canyon of the Apurimac would stay the Incas. And now . . .

They cut the cables of the bridge and it fell into the water. Later the Inca put it up again. Time passed. Inca Roca died, and another Inca took his place. And he in turn was succeeded by another Inca. Still the Chancas waited and grew stronger. They waited until the Inca was old, infirm, and not able to give battle. Then one night—it was in the year 1438—they attacked.

They crossed over the bridge and moved east toward Cusco. It is sixty miles from the Apurimac to Cusco, and all along the way the Chancas killed and burned Inca towns and people. Soon they ringed the city. The old Inca was so terrified that he and many others fled Cusco under cover of darkness and took refuge in a small fortress in the high Andes. His son, however, did not leave. He was fearless. He called on the very stones of Cusco to rise up, become people, and help him to defend their holy Cusco.

The Chancas, beating their drums, yelling and shouting, shot fire-arrows into the grass roofs of the houses and the city became a sea of flames.

The enemy thought that they had at last won. The Inca had fled, Cusco was in flames, and they could see the armies retreating. But the Incas were not retreating. Without being noticed, they had gotten reinforcements from another valley. They were melting into the darkness, then going around to come upon the Chancas from the rear.

Most of the Chancas had stopped fighting; they thought that the war was won. They were drinking out of the gold cups they

had found, and many were drunk on *aca*-beer. The captains could do nothing to control their warriors. It was at this moment that the Incas attacked from both the front and rear. The Chancas could not retreat, so many were horribly killed. Those who lived were tied up and marched into Cusco.

That wonderful city was one of dead and dying. The roofs were still smoldering, sending up clouds of smoke into the blue sky. The stone-paved streets were filled with the dead who had given their lives to save their city. The Golden Enclosure had been sacked; its gold animals had been torn up and carried away.

Now the Incas had their revenge. They recovered their treasures and the victory. The chieftains of the Chancas were made to lie down, and one by one the Inca chieftains walked over their necks, as if to grind them into the earth. This was the symbol of victory.

The warriors wanted to kill all the captured Chancas, but the son of the Inca would not allow it. "We may," he said, "conquer by arms, but we must reconcile with kindness."

He let most of the Chancas return to their homes, keeping the chieftains as hostages. Only those whom he knew had stolen and pillaged did he kill . . . and in a horrible manner.

They were hung up by their arms and skinned alive. Then their skins were tanned with ashes rubbed into them and by exposure to the sun. After that, the royal carpenters cleverly made a man's figure out of basket reeds, and the skins of the dead were mounted over these wickerwork bodies. The part around the stomach was left hollow; the rest of the figure was stuffed with straw. The stomach, stretched tightly, became a drumhead. When all was ready, these figures were paraded about the plaza and the drums were beaten by the priests. Out of the mouths of these bodies, open by death, came a dull, hollow sound. After this the figures were set up on display outside of the city as a warning to anyone who might again dare attack holy Cusco.

A few days after the victory the old Inca gave up his throne. He had disgraced himself by fleeing. Everyone knew this, and when he died he was buried with few honors.

No one needed to guess who would be the new Inca. The nobles, the priests, the people, all seemed to know that the one most worthy of this was the man who had saved Cusco. After bowing before the image of the Sun, the priests wound a woven sling around his head. Into it they placed a red pompon set into a pin of gold so that it stood out over his forehead. Then a fringe of vicuña wool, dyed red and woven into small, delicate golden tassels, was inserted into the headband. The fringe hung down like a bang across his forehead, almost into his eyes. This was the royal fringe, the "crown" of empire. As the fringe was laid over his head, he said, "I shall take the name of Pachacuti."

And that meant "Earthshaker."

"I, PACHACUTI..."

FOR TWENTY YEARS thereafter the Indians heard over and over again the new laws that began: "I, Pachacuti, decree . . ."

There had been no greater Inca than he, nor any greater organizer. He made new laws and saw to it that they were kept. If a man who was one of the Big Ears did wrong, he was punished, and even more severely than a common Indian. "A noble should know better," said Pachacuti. To steal was to die. "It is just that he who is a thief should be put to death." There was no reason for theft in the empire. If a man was hungry, he could obtain what he needed from the public stores; if he wanted anything badly enough, he could work for it. But the Inca had those who were judges note the difference between stealing for gain and stealing for hunger. If the latter occurred, the chieftain who ruled the Indian was himself guilty. "It would be his

48

fault, so let him be punished, for it was his failure to see that food was not on hand."

Taxes were made equal. There was no money, so the tax each Indian gave was to be in work-service, a *mita* of his time; some worked on the road, while others helped to construct buildings, dams, aqueducts, and storage places. Still others went to work in the mines. "But because the work is onerous, I, Pachacuti, decree that it shall be only for a few months; then the men will be rotated."

Nobles were not to be taxed, nor were any members of the imperial family taxed. But they had to serve as governors, generals, and servants of the realm. Since Cusco had to be rebuilt, Indians who showed promise were made architects. They paid no tax. Nor did the goldsmiths, the Sun Maidens, the priests of the Sun. All others, however, all *purics,* or able-bodied people, paid tax, tax by work.

When Cusco was rebuilt and the laws put into effect, Pachacuti went to war. First he went to the southeast. There lay Lake Titicaca. It was 130 miles in length and forty miles wide. It was so deep that no one had yet found its bottom. It was full of fish and the land surrounding the lake was very fertile; it was occupied by hard-working farmers. And good fighters too. They put up a long resistance to the Incas, but at last they were conquered and the way to Chile was open. But Pachacuti did not push his conquests down to Chile; this he left for his sons.

That being done, he turned to the west. The warm desert coast was two hundred miles across the mountains from Cusco. To break through, to conquer those people, he had first to take on the Rucanas once again. His troops fought long and hard against the Rucanas. Small and robust, they fought hard to keep their lands. At last they lost and the way was open to the coast.

Then Pachacuti said, "Let them be reconciled to us by kindness."

The Inca sent his legions to build the road that led to the coast. The road followed the rise of the western Andes and crossed it.

Pachacuti himself planned this road. It was one of the joys of his life. For the Inca admired order and orderliness, and roads were one of the important links of the empire. The roads brought new peoples together, and trade flowed over them. And if newly conquered tribes dared revolt, the Inca could send troops over these roads quickly and end it all.

The *quipu-camayoc* stopped telling his history. He picked up another *quipu*. He paused, counted as he went through the strings, separating the colors. He remembered. Yes, it was in the year 1450 that the royal road to the sea was completed. Pachacuti was then forty-eight years old (Ayri counted his strings to be sure that he was right) and he had been Inca (again Ayri counted other strands) for twelve years.

When the Inca Pachacuti reached Chala on the edge of the sea, he built a huge depository there to store dried fish, mollusks, and seaweed. The place was built near a bay, a deep inlet of the sea, which was full of sea creatures. Small octopi swam freely about; seaweed grew on the rocks and could be gathered at low tide. At the bay he ordered a village built, and behind it he had the great storage rooms erected.

The road from Chala was the most direct road to Cusco from the sea. Its governor sent the Inca fresh fish daily. The fish was wrapped in seaweed, put in sacks made of llama wool, and carried by *chasquis* to Cusco. Every two and a half miles the *chasqui* would be relieved by another who waited at the edge of the road. Thus, a relay of about eighty *chasquis* got the fresh fish from Chala to Cusco—a distance of two hundred miles—in two

days. Since the road climbed from sea level to 10,000 feet within the first five hours of running time, the fish stayed cool and fresh.

With two of the four directions in order, Pachacuti now turned his eyes to the north. First, Pachacuti remade the great suspension bridge, the Huaca-chaca. Then he built three others across the deep chasm of the Apurimac. All the tribes in the area then came and made peace with him.

As was his custom, the Inca first sent out his ambassadors who told of the greatness of their Inca and the tribes that he had conquered. Then they spoke of their religion, the Sun. The ambassadors said that if the Indians who were now the enemy of the Incas became part of the empire, a highway would be built into their lands. They could keep their customs, dress, even their own chieftains, but they would have the Inca's protection.

Inca Pachacuti had really shaken the earth of Peru. Now he was tired of warring. He went back to Cusco and left further military conquests to his son.

The Inca Empire had changed so quickly that it was hard for the people to realize how great they had become. Only a few years before, the Incas had been so weak that the Chancas had thought it was nothing to attack sacred Cusco, which they would have taken had the Incas not rallied under the man who later became their ruler. Twenty years later, after many battles, the Incas controlled all the land from Lake Titicaca to Lake Chincha, a distance of one thousand miles. They dominated the eastern Andes and beyond this eastward to the edge of the high jungles, the *yungas*. By 1461 old Pachacuti was, as he said, "full of years." Fortunately, he had many sons trained to carry on the empire.

One of the sons, Topa Inca, had already made a raid on the city-state of Cajamarca to test their defenses. Cajamarca was a large, independent tribe and the only one that could stop the Incas from sweeping north into Ecuador. The city lay in a warm valley at over 8,000 feet. It was famous for its hot sulphur springs. Many an old chieftain asked permission "to take the baths" at Cajamarca.

This tribe had an importance beyond its size, for the rivers which poured down to the hot, rainless coast were controlled by them. Chan-Chan, the capital of the Chimú Empire—rivals of the Incas—depended on that water. Without it, all of their desert gardens would burn under the pitiless sun. So the Great Chimú, as they called the Chimú king, made a treaty with Cajamarca. He said, "If the Incas attack you, it will be the same as if they attacked us."

The Incas were not set back by this. They knew that the

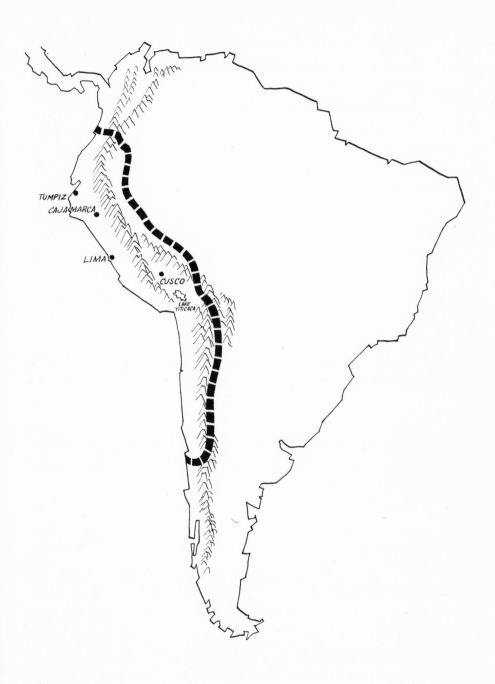

TUMPIZ

CAJAMARCA

LIMA

CUSCO

LAKE
TITICACA

Chimú warriors from the coast would not fight well in the high Andes, because they were too unused to the cold. Topa Inca gave over part of the great Inca army to his brother, General Capac Yupanqui. In that army were various tribes, some Inca and others who had only recently been conquered. One was the Chanca tribe, the same people who had attacked Cusco in 1438. After Pachacuti killed many of their chieftains he tried to win over the remainder of them. He allowed them to fight with his army and gave them their share of booty. He even allowed them to keep their own leaders. He did everything to win over the old enemy, but they were not to be easily won. A few days before they were to go to war against Cajamarca the whole army disappeared: women, children, warriors, even llamas. They took the ancient route to the east toward the jungles and disappeared.

When he heard this, Pachacuti was in a high rage. To Topa Inca, who would soon succeed him, he said, "Son, you now see the many great tribes that I will leave you. And you know what great work this has cost me. Mind that you keep them in the empire and even add more to it. No one must raise his eyes against you and live, even if he be your own brother." Topa Inca well understood. Because his own brother had allowed the Chancas to escape, he ordered him executed.

"It is well," said old Pachacuti when he heard of it. "I, Pachacuti, did not make laws to frighten my people. I made them to be enforced . . . even against my own son."

In 1461 Topa, now the tenth Lord-Inca, lay siege to Cajamarca. Even though the Great Chimú sent troops up from the coast as he had promised, the "town in the valley" fell to the Incas. The whole northern part of the country was now open to them as far north as Quito. And to Quito, Topa Inca sent his armies. They fought, conquered, and then rebuilt the cities in Inca fashion. Highways were built and the *chasqui*-runner system was set up. As fast as he toppled other tribes, just as fast did the Inca weave those tribes into the Inca Empire.

All this very much pleased the Great Chimú, for he thought that as long as the Incas interested themselves in the north they would not molest him and his desert kingdom.

The Chimús were the Moon Kingdom. The Incas were the Sun Kingdom. They were great rivals and there was a reason for this.

The Chimús—who called themselves the Kingdom of Chimor —were coastal dwellers. The sun was almost always there, burning, baking, heating everything under its brazen glare. There was no need to pay homage to it; it was always there. Yet as the Chimús fished the sea and reckoned with tide and time, they saw that the moon had something to do with the tides, the waves, the fish in the sea. The moon was their first god.

In a way, water was a problem, since it never rained on the coast. It had to be brought down by aqueducts from rivers in the high Andes; the Chimús had no other source of water. Thus, the god of water was important to them. Of rock, they had little or none. They built their houses and their cities of sun-dried mud.

The Incas did not always have the Sun. The Sun made their cold lands warm, so the Sun was their god. The Sun was their religion. Since the Incas did not live near the sea, the moon meant less to them. As for water, rain came in its measured time. Thus the water gods were not so important. Rock was the Inca's building material, and they worshiped it almost as a god; they loved to take a piece of rock and chip it with their stone hammers, polishing it until it gleamed like metal.

So these two rivals differed in their gods and in their way of life. They were also rivals in power. The Chimús held the coast from the center of Peru up to Tumpiz where the desert melted away into the jungles of the north. And in order to insure their water supply, they made alliances with other tribes, the Cajamarcas, for example.

Now, these facts of life made the Chimús and Incas enemies. If the Incas were to make themselves masters of all Peru and beyond, they must remove the Cajamarcas.

So even after the Cajamarcas were defeated, the Great Chimú sat in his capital Chan-Chan, believing that the Incas had gone north and would leave them alone. That is precisely what Topa Inca wanted him to think. He sent his generals to the north and he doubled back. The Inca moved his troops down to the coast, following a river, and in this way he came to Tumpiz.

Tumpiz lay in the coastal desert not far from where the river ran into the sea. The land was well cultivated. The Tallanes, the people of Tumpiz, were tall, darker than most Indians, and famous for the gold rings they wore in their noses. They were good farmers and good sailors. They had balsa-log rafts, which they sailed. The Chimús had made a friendly conquest of them;

they were allowed to keep all of their own, yet they had to pay tribute to the Great Chimú, six hundred miles south at Chan-Chan.

The Tallanes were so amazed to see the Incas that they forgot to fight. So the Incas moved quickly south toward Chan-Chan and soon stood before the walls of that city.

At first sight the Incas were struck dumb by the size of Chan-Chan. They had never seen anything like it for beauty and splendor. The roads to it were well-kept roads, just like their own. Immense forts crowned all the hills, and temples built of sun-dried brick were everywhere.

Chan-Chan covered eight square miles and was perhaps four times the size of Cusco. The coastal road came right up to its walls. These were immense, made of mud plastered over and painted blue. There were eight walled areas, behind which the various clans lived. Immense pyramids rose above the walls. To the east was the blue of the ocean and the rumble of the waves. Everything was on a large scale. Women wove textiles, and there was a whole clan of goldworkers. Pottery makers not only made pieces by hand, but they had clay molds. Pottery was produced in large quantities.

The Inca sent his ambassadors up to the wall and demanded that the Great Chimú yield. They came back with their eyes torn out. Angry, the Topa Inca ordered his troops to scale the walls. No sooner were the ladders against them than the Chimús knocked them down. The Inca himself was struck by a stone. Many men were lost.

How long was the road the Incas had traveled! Young Huamán, hearing the story from the lips of a man who had taken part in it, had not realized that the *quipu-camayoc* had stopped talking. All that could be heard was the small, birdlike chirp of the *cuis* as they scurried about. . . .

The old man filled his mouth with a new wad of coca leaves. He dipped his lime stick into the gourd of lime and put it into his mouth several times. He waited for the coca to take effect. Then he leaned back, taking his *quipu.* He counted the knotted strings, sat back, and closed his eyes.

"Yes, it was 1466 during the month of Paucar Huaray, the month of the earth ripening, that the Topa Inca took his walk in the desert."

He was thinking of water. Without it, Chan-Chan must wither and die. And where did the water come from? Why, from the Andes. And who controlled the Andes? Why, he, the Topa Inca, controlled it. Now if the water . . .

The next day he sent a thousand of his soldiers far up the valleys to where the Chimús had diverted the flow of a river into the aqueducts. The Incas changed the flow of the water; it leaped over the aqueduct, rushed down, and poured into the sand.

The Inca then went up to the walls of Chan-Chan. His men blew a long blast from their conch shells. He asked to be heard. The Great Chimú appeared on the high walls, adorned by a golden crown with tall tapers of gold. Around his neck was an immense golden necklace, and his earlobes were widened to admit a golden ornament patterned with flying birds.

"I am Topa Inca," said the son of the Sun. "I have domination over the air and the waters. I have taken your water from you, and I will keep it until you surrender the Kingdom of Chimor."

It is said that the Great Chimú laughed.

Yet not for long. The water had been diverted. He sent his men out at night to repair the breach, but they were defeated. So the Great Chimú came out from behind his walls and surrendered his whole kingdom to the Inca.

Huamán was amazed by this account of the splendor of the Chimús. He had thought the Incas had brought everything to the world. If they had, then how was it that they found so many other tribes with great cities, with roads, and with goldworkers?

The night air grew cold. His mother rose off her haunches and threw some dried *taquia* into the brazier. The fire blazed; then a faint pungent odor filled the home and the brazier glowed redly.

The *quipu-camayoc* talked on.

"But that was only one of the acts of Topa Inca." He was filled with ambition to outdo his father, so after returning from his great triumph over the Chimús, his armies penetrated into Chile.

There was opposition, but Topa Inca overcame it all. He sent his army down, far down into Chile. They stopped at a river called Maule, erected boundary markers to show the end of the southern part of the empire, and then on one side they erected a fortress called Purumauca.

So did the empire grow.

Now it was the turn of Topa Inca to feel the weight of his years. He was fortunate to have in his eldest son, who had accompanied him everywhere, just the one to succeed him. He did not wait for his death to have the council select and confirm his choice; he named his son Huayna Capac to be the eleventh Inca.

"At what date had Huayna Capac been selected Inca?" The old man asked the question of himself. He stopped and took up his *quipu*. It was a long *quipu*. The main string was five feet in length; from it hung strings of various lengths. Half-slip knots were tied in various ways: Several knots lay close together; on others there was but a single knot. Some strings were black, others red, still others yellow. All had meaning in numbers or as color-symbols for concepts or objects. After looking at the *quipu* for several minutes he went on: "In the year 1493 Huayna Capac became Lord-Inca. He has been our lord for—" again he calculated on the strings, "for thirty-four years."

Huayna Capac has been using himself up for his people. He pushed the frontiers to and beyond Quito to where there was a natural bridge under which a river flowed. This he named Rumi-chaca—the stone bridge—and here he decided to end the Inca Empire. Huayna Capac ordered his architects to set up great stone pillars. "These mark the northern boundaries of my realm," he said. "Let no one go any farther." A large temple was constructed, and a garrison of soldiers was placed on the hillside.

The empire was as large as it is now. Huayna Capac visited it all, from one end to another, from the Ancasmayo River beyond Quito, down to Chile. He visited his realms in the Gran Chaco, which is the jungle east of Bolivia, and built garrisons to prevent the wild Indians from coming into the realm. He set up two stone pillars in the jungle at Patiti. "These mark my eastern boundaries and my armies go no farther."

But this did not prevent the wild Indians from attacking the soldiers. It was in one of these battles that the white man first appeared. When this information came to Huayna Capac he was very upset. He called in the soothsayers and they killed a llama, took out the liver, and studied it. They looked at the stars and consulted oracles.

No one seemed to know just what to make of it.

The Inca seemed now to be suddenly old. At one time, he had been carried everywhere within the empire in his golden litter. Now he no longer traveled. He stayed in his stone palace at Tumipampa, three hundred miles north of Cajas. He no longer moved.

Huayna Capac was, in fact, dying.

AT THE ROYAL HUNT

THE GOVERNOR had promised the people a *caku*.

This was enough to make them work harder than ever, for nothing so excited them as a royal hunt. For them it would be a long holiday and they would hunt up thousands of animals: deer, vicuña, bear guanacos, fox. The people were not allowed to hunt on a large scale without the Inca's permission. He was afraid they would kill the females, and the animals would lessen. Besides, all of these creatures belonged to the Inca by divine right. They had been created by the Sun God for him and the Sun, which as everyone knew was the Inca's original father.

There had not been a royal hunt for many years, so the number of animals had increased. The wild vicuña, cousin of the llama, now fearlessly came down to eat in the fields. The gray-white fur of the vicuña was highly valued. It was as fine as silk, as warm, when woven, as fire in a brazier. Since these animals, unlike the llamas, were wild, there was only one way to get their fur; they had to be rounded up by a *caku*-hunt.

So in the twelfth month of the Inca year, the month called Ayamarca, the Indians would have their promised hunt. But first they had to put their fields in order.

The Incas had a ceremonial year divided into twelve months. This was a moon calendar, based on the waxing and waning of the moon. Each month had its name and each month its ritual. The Inca New Year's began in December with a great festival. The eighth month—equivalent to our month of July—was the time of purification of the earth. The lands were newly divided. The council of Cajas gathered together to see that it was well done. First, the council kept one third of it for the Inca. This was to be cultivated by the village people and the crops were to be held for the Inca's use. It was with these crops that the Inca paid the army, his architects, all other expenses of the empire. The second third of the land was kept for the Sun; that is, for the religion of the state. The products of this part were sent to the priests to pay for the erection of new Sun Temples, their upkeep, and also to feed the priests and the Sun Maidens. The remaining third was divided among the clan members. It was not divided equally; it was divided justly. That is, when a man married he was given or loaned a *topo* of land. This was a piece of land sixty paces long by fifty wide. When a son was born to him, he was given another *topo,* for a daughter, half a *topo* of land. So the land increased with each child. This was right and just. No one could buy or sell land; it did not belong to him. It belonged to the community. Fathers could not leave their land to their sons, because they did not own it. What they did own was the food produced on the land.

When the land was divided, each plot was marked at its margins by piles of stones. It was a crime to remove the stones

or change the boundary markers. And when it was time to plow
the land and prepare it for the crops, all worked together. First
they plowed the land of the Inca (this was in the ninth month
of the year). The men used a foot plow, the *taccla,* which was a
pole six feet long with a hard point sheathed in bronze and a
footrest. Pressure of the foot on the plow made it enter the
ground and loosen the soil. The men worked backward. Women
followed them, breaking up the earth clods with a hoe. It was
backbreaking work, but the Indians were used to it and enjoyed it.

After the fields of the Inca were prepared, the people plowed those of the land allotted to the Sun, their religion. Then they worked the fields of men who were away to the wars. Finally they planted their own. And always together.

What they grew on the land depended on where they were. In high altitudes, about 12,000 feet, corn does not grow. Here, the potato—the *papa*—was the chief food. There were many types of potatoes and from them the Indians made a great variety of dishes. Below the *puna,* the treeless wind-swept plain, farmers grew corn. They also grew a ricelike grain (*quinoa*) and tuber plants other than potatoes. In the warm valleys they could grow chili peppers, tomatoes, squash, and pumpkin. There were many fruits to be had: wild strawberries—small and sweet— chirimoya—large and luscious—and avocados larger than melons. If they did not raise these crops, they could get them by trade at the weekly fairs.

During the eleventh month (Uma Raimi) the Indians held their ceremonies for rain. If the rains were late, as they had been the year before, would it hold up the royal hunt? Huamán remembered that last year people had gone about dressed in black, wailing and pleading with the gods for rain. A black llama was tied up and left to die of hunger and thirst. It was thought that its pitiful wail would turn the heart of the Thunder God and that he would open up the floodgates of rain.

But this year they were favored by the gods. Dark clouds drifted in from the east, from the direction of the jungle, and gathered over Cajas. Then the rains came. So by the time the Governor arrived to open up the royal hunt, the corn was a foot high and the potatoes were beginning to shove their leaves from under the soil.

Huamán couldn't remember seeing so many people gathered together at one time. They came from all the surrounding areas. They came from Huancapampa, as was shown clearly by the chevron markings on their shields, the symbol of their *ayllu*. There were others from Pumacahua; the device on their shields was the head of a snarling puma. Many carried cloth tents, for if the hunt found them far from dwellings, they would have to brave the cold of night. Within a few days, more than fifty thousand Indians moved forward. The middle section moved slowly; the outward ends swifter so as to form an enveloping flank.

With the beating of drums they went forward. Within a short distance, animals began to appear. Rabbits came out of the thickets. Viscachas, rodents resembling *cuis,* left their rocks and ran before the line. Soon deer appeared and then foxes. A bear, a *ucumari* with white circles about his eyes, was seen ahead. The animals sensed that they were being gradually hemmed in. A *tareka,* a deer with small horns, came close to Huamán. He began to swing his sling about his head, but his father stopped him and took instead his bola, a long rawhide rope with a heavy copper ball at one end and two lighter balls at the other end. Mayta whirled the heavy end about his head, then hurled it. The bola struck the deer at its hind legs. At once the weights whirled around the deer's legs in opposite directions. It fell, completely entangled.

All along the line Indians sprang to action. Birds were snared in the nets. The deer caught were tied up with bolas or clubbed to death. The animals were then left for others to pick up, kill, skin, and prepare. By the early afternoon the ends of the beating line met; the circle was complete. Slowly, almost shoulder to shoulder, they now moved to tighten the circle.

A puma, golden-gray in color, took to a high tree. At once he was surrounded by shouting Indians. They pelted him with stones until, angered, he jumped—right into the extended spears of the warriors.

It was not until late that they closed in on the vicuñas, so fleet of foot they were the last to be surrounded. Smaller than the llama, they had long necks and a mass of grayish-brown fur that hung down their chests. The male, larger than the female, guarded his flock. When he heard the terrible noise of the drums, he shrilled his warning call and darted off. The females followed him. One by one they were brought down by the bolas. On orders, no vicuña was to be killed. When caught, they spat and kicked with their powerful legs and sharp hoofs. All this was in vain. Trussed up with bolas, they soon lay on the grass in a position that made it possible to cut a few handfuls of their fine fur. The Indians were careful not to cut too much of the golden fleece; it was this that kept the animal warm in the snow-bound Andes. After the shearing, the vicuñas were released.

For many days thereafter, the people in all the villages and towns worked at the preparation of the meat. First, the animals were evenly divided among all those who had taken part in the hunt. The best of the animals went, as usual, to the Inca. Guanacos were caught. Guanacos were one of the four animals distantly related to the primitive camel who lived in the Andes. Guanacos and vicuñas were wild; one was used for meat, the other only for its fine, silky fur. The Indians said that the llama had developed from the guanaco, which looked like the llama. It had a long neck, a harelip, and its feet were two-toed.

With the guanacos were deer of several kinds, bears, foxes, opossums, and pumas. The largest catch was among the order of Rodentia—rabbits, viscachas, wild *cuis,* and the much-sought-after chinchillas. Of these, Huamán had captured several alive and had put them into a cage.

After the animals were skinned and the hides tanned, the workers turned to prepare the meat. This was cut in long, thin strips and left to dry in the sun. As it dried it turned dark, yet it kept its flavor; when dried it was known as *charqui.* By the time all this was done, the Indians were ready for the market.

THE CATU-MARKET

A MARKET was held three times each month. It was at the same time a market where people exchanged products, a fair, and a festival. Indians came from other places—the coast and the jungle—to trade, and often games were played and there was music and dancing.

Catus were very ancient. People in the Andes and on the coast had held them long before the Incas appeared. The Incas, however, brought them to order: "I, Pachacuti, decree that a *catu* will be held three times monthly. For if people work too long without a stop, it is bad. Let there be a *catu!*"

The market this week was held at Huancapampa, the most important city of the province. Before it was conquered by the Incas, it had been the city of a people called Huancas. They were famous for their feather weavings and their gold. Located at an altitude of less than 9,000 feet, Huancapampa was warmer than most Andean cities. During the day it was warm, even hot. There was a large Sun Temple built of stone in Huancapampa. It was the largest one between Cajamarca to the south and Tumipampa to the north. It was a step-back temple in which each section was set back from the lower part. From a stone doorway, the thirty-three stone steps climbed upward to all the sections. The top was flat and truncated, and on it was a canopy with awnings of beautifully woven cloth. At the time of prayer the priest stood under the canopy and with a golden cup saluted the sinking sun, drinking to its long life.

In front of the Sun Temple were other buildings. They were all much alike, low stone buildings with niches. This window was peculiar to the Incas. No other Indians used it. It was shaped like a keystone and always built into official buildings. The niche had something magical about it, but its meaning had been lost in the deep, dim past.

All of the buildings were thatched with grass. It was to these buildings that the people of the surrounding area brought their tribute. The storehouses were bursting with foodstuffs, feathers, weapons, sandals, weavings, and gold. There were also buildings in which the Sun Maidens were educated. It was here in the Aclla-wasi, the House of the Virgins, that they were trained for service to the Inca.

The market was held in the large square in front of the Sun Temple. The edges of the plaza were paved of stone, but the center was of hard mud stamped down for centuries by countless feet.

People arrived early; in fact, some came while the stars still filled the skies. They were of many different tribes and the *curaca* of the city was there to receive them. They had journeyed up the mountains, from the coast and from the jungle. There were Tallanes from near the sea at Tumpiz. Golden rings hung

through their noses, and the women came half-naked. Others came from Chira and some from Zaran, also on the coast. It was from Zaran that a road ran up the Andes to join the mountain highway at Cajas. The coast people brought many things from the hot lands, including monkeys. The people loved monkeys. When the Indians could get a hold of them they allowed the monkeys to live in their houses, eating with them and sometimes even sharing their beds with them. The coast people also brought gold dust in duck quills, jaguar teeth for necklaces, puma skins, jaguar pelts, and food.

It took these people two days to climb up from the coast. On arrival they ate at the *tampu* and from there went on to the market. The section of the market they visited depended on what they sold. At the fruit section an Indian paid for his place and the use of a small cotton awning. Under it the women arranged the things they wanted to trade. Even before the sun painted the world with a pinkish glow, things were on show. There was papaya as round as one's head, yellow inside, cool and sweet to eat. *Pacai* was a long, bean-shaped pod with a sweet-tasting pith. Chirimoyas were olive-green in color and covered with a rough skin; the fruit tasted like strawberries. Little boys wandered about munching chirimoyas, spitting out the hard black seeds.

In another part of the market were the staples, the basic things they ate. There were potatoes, corn, *yuca* (manioc), *oca, quinoa.* Each woman sat on a mat under a white awning. If she sold potatoes, they were built up into small, neat piles in front of her. If she were selling *chuñu,* it was left in an open brown bag so that buyers could see it. In other sections, men were noisily trading animals both tame and wild: pigs, *cuis,* ducks, monkeys, guanacos.

Those things made with their own hands and not part of the tribute tax were considered the makers' very own and could be traded. In different parts of the market, people traded llama skins and ropes made from the hides; sandals; deerskins; rock salt; pepper ground from seeds of the *molle* tree, or *achiote* (a seed used to dye cloth and food red). There was a large section for weavers and weavings. Alpaca wool cloth could be bartered for in long pieces or in ready-made tunics. The alpaca, the fourth of the llamalike animals, was the real wool-producer. Llama wool was too greasy to be used for good weaving; it was used for ropes and cargo bags. Alpaca wool is thick, white, and long-stapled. Alpacas were herded, like sheep, in immense flocks in the high, cold *puna* (the cold Andean prairies about 13,000 feet above sea level). Almost all wool garments, blankets, and tapestries were made of alpaca wool.

People also sold *charqui:* sun-dried llama meat. But there was also duck, monkey, deer, tapir, or fish. So it was to this section that the family of Mayta came. As Cajas was only a short way from Huancapampa, they did not have to set off as early as many others who had come from long distances.

Luxuries too had their place. Feathers for a headdress, earrings of stones and shells, were luxuries. People walked miles or traveled for days, even weeks, to get them. Was not perfume a luxury? Indian women wanted this very much. They spent days and nights weaving beautiful rugs to trade for sticky, stinky resin that attracted flies as often as it did the sought-after attention of men. Traders offered shells, for it was from mother-of-pearl that jewelers cut out the pieces which became necklaces or arm bands. Coral was carved and strung between jaguar teeth; such a necklace was a charm. The coppersmiths made *tupus,* pins that held together the two ends of a woman's shawl. Both men and women bought feathers—the blue, gold, or green wing and chest feathers of little birds that came mostly from the Amazon—which they would weave into cloth. *to make designs.*

At the market, Huamán had his chores to do. He had to help erect a white cotton awning over his mother's head, for the glare of the midday sun was strong. He also helped to carry the things she would barter. And later he brought a large bowl of *aca* and set it down near her so that she could slake her thirst. This finished, he walked up and down the rows of sitting women to watch them sell. There was no fixed price; people bartered with one another. Consider, for example, the woman who was selling her beans in exchange for potatoes. She sat down opposite the woman selling potatoes under the shade of the white awning.

In front of the pile of potatoes she piled three handfuls of beans. They were pretty beans, kidney-shaped and of mottled color. The potato trader shook her head; the amount of beans offered was not enough for the pile of potatoes. So the woman added half a handful more beans to her pile. Still the potato woman shook her head. After a moment, the woman put a few more—maybe five or ten—beans on the pile. Finally, the potato woman was satisfied. She pulled the beans toward her, putting them into a cloth bag. The other woman gathered in the potatoes. Not a word had been exchanged between them. Then the potato woman gave the buyer two small potatoes in addition. This was the *yapa;* after a trade or sale, the seller gave something extra.

So the market went the whole day.

Since boys Huamán's age were not expected to work all the time, there was time for play. Near the Sun Temple, boys were playing *taucca-taucca,* an ancient game of "pile on." Having chosen sides, the boys would pile on top of one another, the lower ones trying to scramble free and pile on top again. So it went until, tired and dirty, they would rest and drink. Others played at *papa-awaki*—"potato-chief"—which was played with a rubber ball. The ball was bounced about until one caught it and became the "chief." The smaller boys liked to spin tops. The wooden top was set spinning, and was kept spinning by being whipped with a small whip. It took great patience to learn how to do this. It was played mostly by small boys; most of the older ones, like Huamán, played at *conkana.* It was played somewhat like the game parchesi. A board was marked with five sections, each counting ten, twenty, and so on. Each player used a bean of a different color. The players threw wooden dice marked with numbers and moved their beans along the playing board accordingly.

War games were the best liked. Boys were always playing

"war." They made shields exactly like their fathers' except that theirs were smaller. They had lances blunted with rubber and bolas which they threw at each other as they charged, just as the grown-up warriors did.

At the end of the market day, before the people departed, was the proper time to announce any new laws or to relate what was happening in the empire. It was then that the *curaca* gave out the news in the Rimac-pampa, the Speaking Plaza. There, mounted on a platform, he told the people that their Inca Huayna Capac was ill. No one knew what manner of evil spirits possessed him. The best of the *hampi-camayocs*—medicine men—were now with him. Many of the Inca's generals were also at Tumipampa.

The strangers whom the Indians called Viracochas, the people who had come in a strange ship out of the sea, were now gone. They had been in this land for twenty-four days. They had done no harm, having traded strange clothes and different kinds of necklaces they had brought with them in exchange for gold and silver. They had taken eight Tallanes tribesmen from Tumpiz, six llamas, and many other things. The Viracochas had left behind two of their own people: one with a white skin and a long reddish-black beard, the other with a jet-black body, which looked painted but was not . . .

And then the *curaca* announced exciting news, exciting at least for the girls. At the next fair, which would fall within thirteen days, the Governor would make his annual inspection tour. During this time there would be dancing and festivals, and he would arrange new marriages. He would also select young girls to be trained as *Ñustas,* or Sun Maidens.

PEOPLE OF THE SUN

THE DANCES had been in progress for hours before the Governor arrived. Dancing was part of Inca worship. There were many of them, including the Dance of the Birds and the Procession of the Puma, the Procession of the Monkeys, and the Procession of the Bears. In one, men danced masked like condors, wearing condor wings on their arms; they whirled slowly around, like a condor in flight, while drummers kept the beat. The drums were of various sizes; the large one was of llama hide stretched tightly across wood. There were smaller drums made of snake or iguana hides. There were *tinya,* drums made like tambourines, with a drumhead on one side and copper rings on the other. Flutes were many and various. The small six-note *antara* could be played with one hand while the musician beat a small drum with the other.

There were also big flutes: the four-note *quena* made from bamboo was as tall as a man. It made a booming sound. When

77

the men danced the Deer Dance they were masked to look like deer and the mask had real antlers. The musicians also had antlers mounted on a drum which they beat to give rhythm. When the Dance of the Llama came, the people became almost tearful from laughter. For each llama skin there were two men, one for the front legs, the other for the rear. They imitated the llama getting up, sitting down, running, even spitting. For this dance, the musicians used the lower jawbones of llamas. When these bones lay long in the sun, the large teeth became loose; therefore, when the jawbone was struck it gave out a strange, rattling noise.

There were many dances that day. Every village had its own specialty. If the people lived in the higher Andes, where the condor lived, they did this type of dance. If they came from warm parts, like the *yungas,* they performed dances of birds, foxes, or deer. In every dance the dancers were masked. For it was not only for fun and joy that they danced; they danced for the gods. Animals had souls, too. The Indians knew that it was wrong to kill animals; they did it through need. When they killed they kept the skull of the animal with great reverence and they made masks to resemble the dead animal. They were careful to learn the habits of each animal and the noises it made. In the dances they mimicked these. The dead animal would be pleased at how much the people thought of them; they would allow their kind to be killed again. If not, if the Indian showed disrespect, the animals would not allow themselves to be killed. They would run away, and the Indian would have no meat.

The people of Cajas were performing the Farmer's Dance when the *apo* arrived. The male dancers were masked to look like actual people living in Cajas. One mask showed a broken nose. One had two long real hairs stuck in the chin of the mask.

Everyone knew that this dancer was supposed to be Yaya, the old uncle who sat in the sun, too old to work, spending the day pulling at the two long hairs on his chin. Women were also masked. The men used the foot plow in the dance; the women bent forward and made motions to show that they were breaking up clods of earth with thick-headed clubs.

The dance was almost finished when there was a blast of horns. It was the Imperial Governor. He was carried on a litter and was proudly greeting the people by inclining his golden halberd. His headdress was simple, a woolen band wound around his head; his ears were decorated with golden ear spools. Around his throat was a golden necklace.

Warriors with tall lances protected him. Many other nobles walked behind him. The Imperial Governor was a brother of the Inca and was coming in the Inca's name. Therefore he was welcomed as the Inca would have been. The people in the plaza fell into deep silence, knelt, and touched the ground. The litter was let down at the stone doorway of the Sun Temple. Very proud, as if he were the Sun God himself, the Governor walked very slowly up the thirty-three stone steps to the top of the temple. He sat down in one of the seats which had been carved out of a single piece of stone covered with gold plate.

The *curaca* of the town came to pay him homage. He slipped off his splendid tunic, wearing instead a simple one used by the common Indians. He took off his sandals. Then he put a light load on his back. In this way the *curaca* of Huancapampa welcomed the Imperial Governor. It was the custom. All must show that they were humble before the Inca or the Inca's representative.

It was an important moment. The officials were here to choose from all the surrounding districts the young girls who were worthy. If chosen, they became *Ñustas,* the Sun Maidens. It was one of the greatest honors that could befall a family.

An Indian generally was no more to the Inca than a number on one of the counting strings on a *quipu.* The Inca did not know his people by name. Each was known only as one of a number of people living in a certain place. Men could live and die on the same land without ever leaving it. They were told when to marry, when to plow, when to harvest, when to weep. It is true that some advanced because of their talents; they were able to become soldiers, medicine men, or priests. Women had no such fortune. They married, they had children, they worked, and they died. All, that is, except the *Ñustas.* A girl of the lowliest family, if comely or talented, could be taken from her humble home, educated, and then married to some famous man. It was natural that this excited everyone, especially the young girls ready to be chosen.

First, the marriages were arranged. No one in the realm was allowed to remain single. Bachelors were just not allowed, and for a simple reason. The wealth of the Inca was in his people. The more there were, the stronger he became, and as the people were the source of his wealth (for they paid taxes in work-service), any man who did not marry and beget children robbed the Inca of taxes due him. Therefore, all must marry. As a rule, a girl married at sixteen, men at twenty. That seemed a good age. The *curacas* called out the names of all those qualified to marry who were still single. In most cases, girl and man had already chosen each other. If they had not, the Governor chose a husband for the girl. Then, holding their hands, the Governor blessed the wedding.

The *Apopañaca*—"He-who-chooses-the-girls"—now came forward. As the names of all the girls who had reached ten years of age were called, they marched forward in a single file. Many hoped that Curi would be selected. She was the eldest of Huamán's younger sisters, very pretty and talented. She was dressed like her mother in a long dress that almost reached her ankles. On her head lay a piece of finely woven cloth folded into a square of four folds with a longer piece hanging down the back to cover her braided hair. A mantle of purple wool was thrown across her shoulders and held together at her breast by a *tupu*, a large pin with a flattened head. Most girls of her class wore copper *tupus*, but Curi's was of gold. And that is why they called her Curi, for it was the name for "gold." She had been given this *tupu* at her birth, and it was her proudest possession. The head of the *tupu* was perforated with holes into which tiny copper bells had been set. They tinkled when she walked.

She had often heard about the *Ñustas,* for every young girl learned about the Sun Maidens. To one of lowly birth it offered the one chance of change. The chosen ones went to the Acllawasi, the House of the Virgins. There, under the supervision of older women, they learned to weave the silken fibers of the vicuña. They learned how to brew *aca*-beer for the priests, to cook, to weave garments of feathers and gold, to wait upon the Inca, to attend the priests, to enter the Sun-mysteries of their religion, and really to become People of the Sun. When they reached sixteen years of age, one of several things might happen to them. If they felt the mysteries of their religion and showed it, they would become attendants to the Sun Temples. If one was very beautiful, the Inca himself might choose her to be one of his secondary wives. For although he had but one queen, the *coya,* he allowed himself others to attend him. Or one of the Inca's family might fall in love with a *Ñusta,* or a great general might see her. Being a *Ñusta* held much promise.

Curi was brought forward to stand before "He-who-chooses-the-girls." She looked very small before so great a man. She kept her feet close together, her hands clasped in front of her, and her eyes cast down, as she should. Questions were asked about her character, her weaving, her manners, and her morals. When he was satisfied, the *Apopañaca* had her stand aside. Curi had been chosen. The girls who were not chosen became known as the "left-out" girls. When they were sixteen they would marry as did the others on this day.

When Mayta's family returned to their home in Cajas, they left little Curi behind. She had entered the House of the Sun Virgins at Huancapampa. There she would remain until she was sixteen.

Curi's first duties were to learn all about the Sun, the religion of the Incas. First there was Viracocha, the Creator God. He created everything, including the void. The Sun, Inty, was his most important servant. He warmed the earth and made the crops grow. Inti was always represented in the Sun Temples as a golden disk with rays and a human face. Next was the Thunder God. He brought rain, without which nothing grew. His image in the Sun Temple was that of a man holding a club. He was called Illapa. And next came the moon. She was the wife of the Sun and was known as Mama-kilya (moon mother). She was important because she regulated time and the Inca months; the calendar was based on the waxing and waning of the moon. The Inca people never understood why she grew and declined, but when she was in eclipse they thought that she was being eaten by a serpent. It was the duty then of the Sun Maidens to beat drums, thus making noise to scare off the serpent.

Silver was the symbol of the moon's tears; thus the moon was always represented as a silver crescent. And then there were the stars, so numerous that many had names known only to the high priests. There were the Pleiades, a cluster of stars seen very clearly in the Andean nights; the Incas thought that they watched over the seeds of growing plants. (They called them *Kolka*, which meant "granary.") There were many other gods: the earth mother, the sea mother, and the gods that watched over the people, as well as spirits, to see that they came to no harm.

The evil spirit was sopay. Indians had to watch out for him. He brought illness and witchcraft; he made good things bad, but never bad things good. One had to be careful to avoid him and not to do anything to anger him. A very bad *sopay* was one who had a human head but no body. It went about at night saying over and over again, *"wis wis; wis wis."*

Viracocha made man; he created him out of the Sun. The Incas said that the Sun was their father, so when the Lord-Inca lay dying he would say, "I am going back to the Sun, who is my father." All people had souls and all animals had souls; even plants had them. When an Indian died, if he had kept the customs which were the tribal laws, he went to the upper world to live forever with the Sun. There it was eternally warm and there was ample food. Those who did not keep the customs went down into the earth where it was eternally cold, dark, and dismal. They ate stones. But noble people, whether or not they had kept the customs, went to live with the Sun.

There were hundreds of shrines all over the empire. They were called *huacas,* meaning "holy." Many things could be holy: The great bridge Huaca-chaca that crossed the gorge of the Apuri-mac River was indeed *huaca.* The dead became *huacas.* Dead Lord-Incas were great *huacas,* and their mummies were wor-shiped. Caves, springs, mountains, even unusually shaped stones were *huaca.*

In every large city (Huancapampa, for instance) or even smaller ones like Cajas, there was a Sun Temple. They were

usually built of stone and beautifully made. The priests lived at
the side of the temple, and it was their duty to intercede with the
gods. When water was needed a priest addressed prayers to
the Thunder God. With a Sun Maiden aiding him, he would
stand in front of the Thunder God's statue and bow low from
the waist with his arms stretched out in front of him, level with
his head and parallel to each other. Hands open, palms down,
he brought his hands to his lips, kissing them. The Sun Maiden
then brought him *aca*-beer in a golden goblet. He dipped his
fingers in it and flicked it toward the Sun and the moon, pouring
some of it into a silver goblet to be left for the Thunder God.
Then he prayed:

> "O fountain of water
> > which for so many years
> Has watered my fields.
> Through which blessings we gather our food,
> Do the same this year
> Pour down the waters
> > and give it if pleases,
> Even more water
> So that the harvest this year,
> > may be in abundance."

All this and much more did Curi learn. She knew that she was
protected from all evil. There were guards placed at each Accla-
wasi, and no Indian could go within its doors. Safe, and in the
full knowledge that she was safe, she learned all that she must
do so that she could serve the Inca. Curi lived fully each day of
the month.

Yet hardly had she begun to be a *Ñusta,* when Huayna
Capac, the Lord-Inca, died.

THE WHITE-FACED GODS

HUAMÁN HEARD about the death of the Inca when he returned from the fields. As he came into Cajas the drums were sounding and people were weeping. Women with black cloths over their heads were wailing, throwing up their arms in grief; even the men wept openly and unashamed. "We have lost our father," they kept repeating. Their sorrow was very real. Huayna Capac had been a father to them all, and he had been Inca for thirty-four years. During that time he had visited every part of the empire numerous times to inspect it personally. From Chile to Ecuador was a distance of 3,250 miles, yet he covered this distance many times. Now, in the third month of his thirty-fourth year as Lord-Inca, he was dead. The year was 1527.

During the last week before his death there had been much traffic on the Inca road to Tumipampa. Guards were posted by the Cajas bridge to be sure that only those people who had good reason were aboard. From all who crossed they collected a toll.

86

All, that is, except the priests, the generals, and the many members of the imperial family. In the last days, some of the most famous medicine men had gone north to Tumipampa, where the old Inca lay dying.

The *hampi-camayocs* had done everything possible to cure the Inca. First, they blew tobacco smoke about the room to rid it of any evil *sopay* that might be lurking about. Flour made from black maize was sprinkled on the floor; more such flour, moistened, was put on the walls. Then they arranged two pottery braziers in front of the dying Inca. They built fires in them with slivers of wood dipped in llama fat and fanned them into hot coals by blowing through long copper tubes, which acted as a bellows. When the coals were red-hot, the medicine men folded their legs under them and began chewing large wads of coca leaf. The cocaine juice they swallowed soon coursed through their veins, and they began to have visions. They looked into the fire to read what it said. They addressed themselves to the flames: "Tell us, from where comes this disease? What is it? Who has brought this to our Inca?" They bent close to the fire to get the gods' fiery answer.

The medicine men had agreed that the gods indicated that the Inca had been struck down by a pestilence. It was the same disease that was killing many people on the shores of Ecuador. Who, then, was the bringer of this pestilence? To determine this, the medicine men next secured a black llama. It was sacrificed, its lungs taken out and studied. One of the *hampi-camayocs* blew into the lung until it swelled like a balloon, and a maze of veins—small and large, red and black—appeared on its surface. For hours the medicine men hovered over these, trying to read the portents. Then they tried medicine. After that they bled the right arm and then the left. They gave the patient *guayusa*-tea to drink and herbs which all agreed were good. Yet the medicine men had to be cautious. This was the Inca. If anyone were to think he died as a result of their medicine, they could easily be killed.

On the third day they decided to try human sacrifice. The Incas did not use *capac-cocha* often; only when all other means failed. And it was clear that the medicine men were failing. The Inca's face was pale, he breathed very slowly, he was now too weak to eat. Only *capac-cocha* might save him. The priests found two of the most beautiful girls and two of the finest-looking boys in Tumipampa and strangled them with the sacred rope. While still warm and half alive, their hearts were cut out, and from the blood that gushed from them, the medicine men painted symbols on the tunic of Huayna Capac. Yet in a few hours this, too, was known to be hopeless. On the last night of the third month, *Hatun Pocoy,* the month of the great ripening, Huayna Capac, the eleventh Lord-Inca, died.

Within hours the medicine men and the priests were making a mummy of his body. Opening it, they took out his heart, stomach, and all other organs. The body cavity was filled with preservative herbs and fine cloths. Then the wound was sewn up, the legs put into sitting position, and the body wound with white cloth. Only the finest muslin was used. On top of this came heavier white cloth. Then the Inca's robes. Around his neck was placed a necklace of emeralds and gold. The jewelers and carvers worked day and night to make the mask which would be placed over the Inca's face after he was made into a mummy. On his head they placed the royal fringe, which was his crown. Then they placed his mummy on a golden litter and prepared to carry it to Cusco, more than one thousand miles away.

This was the last time Huayna Capac was seen. Where at one time Huayna Capac had sat on his litter, now sat his mummy in his stead. He had become *huaca.* The lances he had used in

his lifetime were placed on his litter; his coca bag and stick, the amulets he used for good-luck charms, all were there. When the mummy of Huayna Capac arrived at Cusco it would be placed in his palace. Then that palace would be closed, and no one would live in it but the mummy of Huayna Capac. An image of gold would be made of him, and he would be served by his many wives just as if he were alive. Food, drink, and coca leaves would be left beside his mummy. If some of his wives wanted to share the other world with him, they would be strangled and buried close by in the wall so that their souls could share his fate in the other world.

At the same time the people were to have a new Inca. Huáscar, now thirty-five years old, was Huayna Capac's eldest son, but the Inca's council of advisers did not always choose the eldest son. They tried to choose the best of the Inca's sons, of which there were many.

Huáscar was not a famous general, for while his father had been away on the many wars that plagued the kingdom, he had run the empire. When his father died, he fasted three days. He neither ate nor drank. And at the end of the three days the priests brough the royal fringe to him.

The ceremonies took place in front of the Sun Temple at the great plaza. The square was full of people. Surrounding Huáscar were most of the powerful chieftains of all the tribes which formed the Inca Empire.

When Huáscar was "crowned" with the royal fringe the people raised their voices to praise him. Nobles from the empire now came forward. They took off their fine tunics and gold ear spools, their necklaces and sandals. On their backs each slung a cargo of maize. This was the symbol of their humility. They bowed before Huáscar, giving him their oath of fealty.

All the great chiefs were there except one. Atahualpa, Huáscar's half brother, the son of a noble woman in Quito, had refused to come. He had been Huayna Capac's favorite son, the one who always accompanied his father to battle. Atahualpa did not come to Cusco with the mummy. There were various reasons given, but it made no difference to Huáscar. He was angry at the insult.

Huáscar was also angry at the evil spirits that had killed his father. As soon as he was made Inca, he ordered the priests and the medicine men who had attended his father brought to him for questioning. What was this disease that had killed the Inca? People knew that no one died a natural death; there was no such thing as natural death. Deaths were not caused by something, but by *someone*. Who was that someone? How sure were they, who knew the spirit world, that the one who killed Huayna Capac might not now kill him—Huáscar?

Now what of those two Viracochas living in Tumpiz? Could they not be the ones who had brought the pestilence? The Inca wondered why they were permitted to live like princes on the coast, surrounded by the women of Tumpiz and served as if they were *curacas*. There was much speculation in the palace of Huáscar. Not everyone thought that the strange white men should be killed. Many, including some chieftains, believed that they might be gods. They feared the harm that might be done if the Inca killed the strangers. There were many different opinions, but the prevailing one was that the Viracochas must die. But in what manner?

What was going to happen was soon known in Cajas because it was here that the connecting road to the coast joined the main road. Not many days later, warriors came up the mountain road from the direction of Tumpiz. On their shoulders they carried a simple litter, only two poles with a rush mat as flooring. On it sat two rigid figures. Both were grinning horribly in death.

One was Alonso de Molina, one of the Viracochas who had been left behind at his own request. Born in Úbeda, Spain, he was a sailor who was looking for adventure and gold; now he had found his death. When his captain, Francisco Pizarro, sailed away to Spain it had been Molina's plan to remain in the Inca Empire so that he could learn the language and the geography of those Indians. In this way Molina would have ample information for Pizarro when he returned to make his conquest. But things did not go quite that way. Molina fell in love with the country. It was like a paradise. People did not live for money; they worked without it, yet seemed content. The women were pretty, some even beautiful. They treated Molina as if he were a *curaca*. In his soul he worried about a conquest which would end this form of life. And so, too, thought Ginés, his companion.

Ginés was a Negro. A slave uprooted from his home in Africa, he had been freed when he saved the life of his patron, a Spanish naval captain. Ginés had then become a sailor, and fate had led him to sail with Pizarro. When he saw the tropical lands and how the people lived, easily and well, he compared this with the life he had led in his own land. Thus he agreed to stay behind with Molina. The Tallanes appreciated him. He was simple, kind, and curious. They could never understand that he was naturally black-skinned. Since Indians sometimes painted themselves black in wartime, children never tired of trying to take off his black color.

When the old Inca Huayna Capac first learned that the ship had sailed away, leaving behind two of the Viracochas, he had invited them to Tumipampa. They were brought over the road that followed the Tumpiz River into the mountains, past the gold mines at Zaruma. A day's walk and they were in Loja. From there it was a four-day walk to Tumipampa, where Huayna Capac maintained his northern headquarters.

No one was exactly certain what had passed between the old Inca and the Viracochas, who had not yet been in the land long enough to learn the Inca language. Yet enough was understood by the Inca to give him a glimpse of the future. The Viracochas made it clear that in some distant land there were many white men like Molina. And that their king was very powerful, that he had many big ships and could come out of the sea bringing men—and yet more men. The Viracochas had terrible war weapons. Also, they worshiped the true God, a God who was different from that of the Incas. Aside from the Inca's inner circle, no one really knew what had passed at this meeting. But after the Viracochas were allowed to return to Tumpiz, the old Inca took sick. He sat for many days talking to no one, eating nothing. Then he died.

Now Alonso de Molina, or what was left of him, sat grinning horribly. He had been strangled and skinned alive, and like the captive Chancas many years ago, his body had been made into a drumhead. It had an almost lifelike appearance—except that where the eyes should have been, there were only dark holes and the mouth remained fully open, as if Molina were laughing at the way life sometimes shows its strange ways. As for Ginés, he had received the same treatment and had been made into a flute player. His arms were bent in front of his chest, and he held a *piroro*-flute in his hands. This flute had been made from his own shinbone. The black color had left his skin; it was now gray, ash-gray. Only the tight, crisp, curly black hair told that he had once been Ginés. In this manner the Viracochas were brought to Cusco.

There were many who thought that this would not cure the pestilence. And if Huáscar, the twelfth Lord-Inca, thought that by killing the Viracochas he had put his danger behind him, he was wrong.

His danger lay in Atahualpa.

ATAHUALPA AND HUÁSCAR
AND THE "BROTHERS' WAR"

WAR WAS not long in coming. When it came, it was a form of war the People of the Sun had seldom known. It was to be the most horrible of wars, brother against brother.

Atahualpa refused to come to Cusco. For one reason, he was naturally proud. Furthermore, when he became a man, he had gone with the Inca's legions. Now twenty-five years of age, he had taken part in many battles, and the Inca's generals liked him because he fought like one of them. In one skirmish he had lost part of one ear, and of this he was very sensitive. Although not tall, he was robust and he walked about even now as if he were the ruler of the kingdom.

After Huáscar was made Lord-Inca he sent his ambassadors to his half brother, asking him to come to Cusco and take the oath. Atahualpa had refused. For two years he made no effort to contact the Inca or render him homage.

Many said there were reasons for this. When Huayna Capac

94

heard from the Viracochas that they came from a land filled with different people, he had grown fearful. He knew that strange things had been going on for some time. Two years before the Viracochas arrived in Tumpiz, a white man with a black beard—one who was named Alejo García, it was said—had been killed in the Gran Chaco. He had been leading wild Indians against an Inca outpost. First, there had been white men with beards from the east; now they came from the west. And even more. When Huayna Capac pushed the frontiers of his empire to the north beyond Quito, he was brought into contact with Indians called Chibchas. They lived in the land where the emeralds came from, trading salt and emeralds for gold dust and cotton. They had heard from other Indians that white men with beards were swarming all over a place called Panamá.

The information he had heard from the lips of Molina, set Huayna Capac thinking. The Inca Empire had grown too large. It was difficult to operate all from Cusco, so it was the old Inca's dying wish that Huáscar should be Inca of the southern kingdom with his capital at Cusco, and Atahualpa be Inca of the northern kingdom with his capital at Quito. Since Atahualpa was the better soldier of the two brothers and his generals liked and trusted him, it would be better if he were in the north— because the danger of a foreign invasion seemed to come from there. It was said that Huayna Capac had given this as his dying wish or command to his council, but that when Huáscar heard of it, he had these advisers put to death so that his dying father's wishes would never be known.

Atahualpa believed that the northern part of the kingdom was rightfully his, but Huáscar said, "There cannot be two Incas." He sent General Atox to capture Atahualpa and bring him to Cusco for the Inca's justice.

Now, in the Inca language, *atox* meant "fox," and the General acted like one. He got a small army into Quito without Atahualpa's knowing what was happening, found him, and captured him. Atahualpa was taken with his arms bound to Tumipampa, the residence-fortress, and there he was imprisoned. Atox then sent messengers to Cusco to inform Huáscar. It took four days for the *chasqui*-runners to relay the message to Cusco, and by the time Huáscar learned that Atahualpa was being held captive, he had escaped.

Full of fury, Atahualpa called up his army and his three famous generals: Rumi-ñahui, Quisquis, and Calicuchima. Rumi-ñahui had gotten his name, meaning "Stony Eye," because he had lost the sight of an eye in battle and it looked as dead as stone. Quisquis had started as a barber, they said, and used to shave the odd hairs that grew on Huayna Capac's chin with a golden-copper *tumi*. Calicuchima was said never to allow any prisoners to stay alive. These three, with their veteran army, met Atox and his men in battle in Ecuador.

In all Andean history, there had never been such slaughter. Atox was captured and thousands of his army were left dead on the field of battle. Atahualpa would not allow them to be buried, and for many years thereafter the field was covered with bones, all that was left when the condors got through with them.

Huamán was in Cajas when Atox's army retreated through it. One of Huáscar's generals ordered Mayta to cut the cables of the bridge after they had passed. Destroy the bridge! Mayta's whole life had been spent keeping the bridge up and in repair. If he had ever destroyed the bridge in peacetime, he would have been executed instantly. There was nothing else he could do, so he had his men cut the bridge, and with tears in his eyes, saw the cables float away into the river. Two days later Atahualpa's

army arrived in pursuit, and Mayta was ordered to rebuild the bridge. So went their world.

Life now was entirely out of joint. Whom should people obey? They had known only one Inca and one law. Now there were two Incas, and the people were at civil war. Many men of Cajas went off to battle. Some fought on one side, some on the other.

The fields were neglected. The royal storehouses were pillaged. The foodstuffs were supposed to be used only in case of famine; now, all that had been stored there was gobbled up by conflict. War affected all. Huamán, now fourteen, no longer played at war; he lived it. He and other boys used real lances with sharp copper points; the bolas which they threw at each other were real and hurt dreadfully when they wrapped themselves around one's legs. Play was becoming the real thing. Huamán learned to dodge rocks hurled at him from slings; he was taught how to use his shield to ward off a blow from a club. He became so expert at throwing a lance that he could strike and kill a deer in full flight.

Another battle was shaping up at Cocha-huaylas. Day and night, supplies went through the town of Cajas, going south to battle toward Cajamarca. Llamas came loaded with maize; other llama caravans carried lances, slings, sandals.

Many of the warriors of Cajas were now fighting on Atahualpa's side. They had been formed into companies of one hundred each, and all of them had the *ucumari* head (the totem of their *ayllu*) painted on their shields. That bear became very famous, for the warriors of Cajas were experts at the lance, and their lances won the battle that day.

Cocha-huaylas lay on a vast plain with a large lake. Huáscar's army was waiting when Atahualpa's army came down the plain shouting, beating drums, and hooting their horns. The lancers went forward, behind them the slingers, who hurled stones over the lancers' heads into the body of the enemy. Stones fell like hail. All over the field, warriors who were struck on head or face dropped to the ground, dead. Huáscar's army replied with their own hail of stones. The two armies closed in. Lancers, shouting "Atahualpa," stabbed at the enemy; men clubbed each other with star-shaped maces. It seemed to be a hopeless swirl of Indians, shouting and killing. Then Quisquis gave the signal for ambush from the top of the hill. Unknown to the enemy and unseen, a whole new army of Atahualpa's lancers came down and crept up from behind. They fell on Huáscar's troops, and that ended the battle. Those who didn't leave their bones for the condors, fled.

Atahualpa passed Cajas a few days later to take up his head-quarters at Cajamarca. People lined the road singing and shouting, for it seemed that he had been victorious. He was carried in a litter and was treated as Inca even though he had not yet received the royal fringe. Atahualpa's face was serious, almost fierce, and he had a very commanding manner. The whites of his eyes were somewhat yellow. His pierced ears were decorated with golden ear spools; in his hand he held a golden mace. Beside him were soldiers carrying a banner like a flag.

Cajamarca was a four-day march from Cajas. A few miles south of it were the famous hot sulphur springs in which all the imperial family bathed. Cajamarca was centrally located with roads connecting it to the coast and jungle. It was a good plan for the army's headquarters, and should they need more warriors, they could get them from the heavily populated surrounding villages.

The war went on, and everywhere it went badly for Huáscar. Defeated on the pampas of Pumpu on the lake now known as Junín, his armies retreated to Jauja, in the center of Peru. Again his armies were defeated. So it went on month after month, year after year, but the end was now close. During the second month of the new year, the month of Huchuy Pocoy, in 1532, the last battle was fought.

Atahualpa's conquering army had now reached the high banks of the Apurimac canyon. On the other side was Huáscar's army, and he himself came out of Cusco to lead it. There were four bridges across the river, all distant from each other. Not knowing just where the main strength of the attacking force would be, Huáscar decided that Quisquis would attack across the Huaca-chaca—the greatest of all swinging bridges—because it was the closest to Cusco. But Quisquis took the longer route because, as he said, "it was the shortest." That is, the shortest to victory. His armies enveloped those of Huáscar, and the battle was fought with intense savagery. It was the end of the twelfth Lord-Inca. He was captured and sent under heavy guard toward Cajamarca where Atahualpa was staying.

Then Quisquis entered Cusco. All of Huáscar's family that he could capture, young as well as old, were hung on poles along the sacred road that led to Cusco. There were, some said, "a thousand or more bodies." Atahualpa was now Inca in everything but name, and this his generals meant to supply. Runners were sent to Cajamarca to carry the victory message to Atahualpa.

But before he had time to celebrate it, another *chasqui* arrived from the coast with an entirely different message: "The Viracochas have returned. This time they have returned with three ships."

Huamán had reached his majority in war.

He was only seventeen, but years of war had hurried up things. He was now a man and a real warrior. The last five years had been years of unhappiness. Not only had the royal brothers fought each other; in Cajas, also, brother had been pitted against brother. For a long time no one knew which of the two Incas to obey. If one Inca ordered a bridge cut, and the command was obeyed, the other Inca might kill the person for having obeyed the first Inca. Life before had been centered about the family. People had lived by customs. If a thing was not to be done, it was not done. The Inca's word had been law. Now people did not know what to do, to which Inca they should give their loyalty. Families became divided, *ayllus* became divided, brother fought against brother. Civil wars, wars between brothers, are always the cruelest because they are the most unforgiving.

Indians were guilty of crimes never before committed. Before, no one would have dared to take food from the royal storage houses; now it was done. Before, no one would have dared to cut down a bridge; now, it was done constantly. Before, no man would have thought of entering the house of the Sun Virgins; now it happened often. At Cajas, even at this time, there were six dead Indians, hanging by their hair. Having tried to get into the House of the Sun Virgins, they had been caught and killed.

Atahualpa's victory brought a feeling of relief. With one Inca victorious, order was again coming back, even though it was slow. A captain sent down to command two thousand warriors was now encamping at Cajas.

Yet, to complicate matters, the Viracochas had returned. Here they were again and at the same place. They had returned in larger force and well-armed. They, too, were busily asking questions: "What happened to the Viracocha called Molina? And where is Ginés, the one with skin as black as soot?" Chilimaza, the chieftain of Tumpiz, invented different answers. What else could he do? Tell them that the Indians had made a human drum out of Molina to beat at their festivals? It was a strange and haunting time.

No one had any idea of what the gods held in store for the People of the Sun.

THE SETTING SUN

THE VERY DAY Huamán was ordered with the other warriors to go to Cajamarca in order to accompany Atahualpa to Cusco, the Viracochas arrived.

It seemed that every new day brought new events. One day the people heard that the brothers' war was over, with Atahualpa the victor; the next day they were brought the news that the strange people had appeared. One day they heard that Huáscar was being sent to Cajamarca—to die. The next day they heard that he was not coming, for as soon as Atahualpa discovered that the strangers had returned, he ordered that Huáscar remain at a town called Andamarca.

Runners and message-bearers came up from the coast in a steady stream. Everything that the white men did was reported. If they built a house, it was relayed to the Inca; if they went hunting with the noisy fire-sticks that sounded like thunder, Atahualpa heard of it. *Chasquis* even brought a piece of paper which had been stolen from the white men by an Indian woman. It had writing on it which no one could understand: "Your Catholic Majesty," it read, "we arrived at Tumpiz on May 15th, 1532 . . ."

And from that day forward everything the white men did was reported to Atahualpa. There were 167 Viracochas this time; all had white skins and most were bearded except the young boys. Most wore metal armor and had metal helmets. The Captain-General, who was called Francisco Pizarro, had a white beard and rode a four-legged animal, very fierce, which was called a horse. There were sixty-seven horses. Three of the men had what the Indians called a *liyapta,* or "thunderbolt," because it made a noise like one and shot out a flame. In addition, twenty men carried small bows. These shot arrows which were no longer than an Indian's arm but very powerful. An arrow from this crossbow could go right through a tree trunk.

Why did Atahualpa not attack them? Why were the white men allowed to remain five months in Tumpiz, building houses and docks for their ships without once being bothered? Did Atahualpa think they were really Viracochas, people of the Creator God who had said he would return one day? Warriors asked this of themselves and of their captains. No one was really quite sure. The soothsayers were burning incense; they studied llama-lungs; they chewed coca leaves; they were doing all they could in order to find the answer. The thing that worried the Generals most was this: The Viracochas seemed to be getting reinforcements from the sea. This had never happened in Peru before. Nothing ever came out of the sea except fish, heavy waves, and an occasional balsa trading craft from Ecuador.

When an enemy was surrounded on the coast, as the Chimús had been, that was their end. There had never been any succor from the sea. The Generals believed—at least some of them did—that the white men, whoever they were, should be killed before more of them arrived.

Atahualpa still did nothing.

In the tenth Inca month—called September by the Viracochas—of the year 1532, *chasquis* brought the news that the small army of Viracochas was at last moving in the direction of Cajamarca. Spies shadowed them all the way. They even knew when a horse threw a shoe; in fact, one was brought to Atahualpa. A month later it was reported that the white men had reached the coastal fortress town of Zaran.

Zaran was a *tampu* stop on the coastal highway. It was a small settlement with many royal storehouses and a fortress of mud brick, located at the crossroads with a lateral road that led to the mountain highway. All of Pizarro's small army settled down at the fort. The *curaca* had been ordered by Atahualpa to see that the foreigners lacked nothing. They were brought food for themselves, grass for the horses.

The Spaniards understood very well what was going on. They had a very good interpreter, a young man they had named Felipillo. He was one of the Tallanes Indians whom Pizarro had taken back to Spain after his first visit five years before. Felipillo had learned Spanish and taught the Inca language to the white men. He now dressed as a Spaniard, though no one could mistake him for one, because he wore a gold ring through his nose and his ears were pierced. Everything that he heard he reported to Pizarro. What he heard at Zaran was that a two- or three-day march would lead to the mountains and the royal Inca road.

On October 8, 1532, Captain Hernando De Soto and forty horsemen took the connecting road to the mountains to discover the royal road of the Incas. De Soto was then thirty-two years old and already a captain of certain renown. He led his forty horsemen up the step-highway to the top of the Andes. Built of stone steps, the road climbed from sea level to 9,000 feet, zigzagging right up the sides of the Andes. Two days later, De Soto and his men rode into Cajas.

Huamán was there, one of the two thousand soldiers awaiting their arrival. News of their coming had preceded them. Nevertheless, when their horses made a spirited entrance into the plaza, people broke and ran. The warriors were under strict orders: "Do not attack the Viracochas, whatever they do." So the Indians stood waiting for their leader to talk with Hernando De Soto.

The Inca war chief was a famous fighter and he seemed afraid of nothing, not even of the horses which snorted in his face. Chosen by Atahualpa for this very delicate mission, he was aware that he must set an example to his warriors. His men were armed, but they must not use their weapons against the white men. He must not insult the strangers, yet he must also be firm.

As ordered, the Viracochas were served *aca*-beer in great wooden beakers. After their ride they were thirsty and very tired. The Inca leader allowed them the use of the royal *tampu* and gave them into the care of five women who would prepare their meals. When De Soto showed surprise at the wonderful road, the war chief called Mayta to be De Soto's guide. De Soto was the first white man ever to see the royal road of the Incas. "It is a road," said he, "made by Indian hands alone; it is broad enough for six of my men mounted on horseback to ride abreast." He saw the bridge, which was Mayta's pride; he noted the guards who were stationed there to take a toll as people passed over it. All this he took down to report to Pizarro, who was waiting for him at Zaran.

As he requested, De Soto was guided south over the Inca highway to the next city, Huancapampa. He seemed amazed by all that he saw and said that the road was as finely made as the Roman road in Spain which he had walked on as a boy.

One month later, farther south, from a place called Zaña, Francisco Pizarro led his small army up the sides of the Andes

along a little-used Inca road. There had been an exchange of ambassadors. Atahualpa had sent his cousin to Pizarro (in hopes of finding out the Spaniards' plans, of course). Pizarro was very attentive and courteous, but of course misled him. They exchanged gifts. The war chief of Cajas, who was still with the Spaniards, had a chance to talk to the ambassador. He had been with the Viracochas for over a month. He had studied them. He knew everyone, some of them even by name.

The war chief said to tell Atahualpa that his warriors should ambush the Spaniards on their way up the mountain road. Every one of them should be killed, because they were false gods; they were not Viracochas, but merely people of a different tribe. All of them should be killed except three. One was a barber who should be saved "because by shaving men he makes them look wonderfully young and hairless"; another was the ironsmith, Juan de Salinas. He shod horses, repaired swords, and knew how to make "thunderbolts"; he would be a good man to have about Atahualpa. The third was a man named Sanchez who was a great jumper. He could vault-jump a horse; he could even make a horse kneel or take salt from his lips. This man should be saved to show Atahualpa how to ride horses and how to vault. All the rest should die!

Yet Atahualpa never ordered the attack. Why? What had he to fear? He was Lord-Inca, surrounded by fifty thousand warriors, veterans of great battles. In his empire there were more than 5 million people, and there were only 167 Spaniards. What could they do against his millions?

On Friday evening, November 15, 1532, Pizarro's small army rode into Cajamarca. The Inca's ambassadors came out to meet them and conduct them to the houses which would be theirs while they remained.

Cajamarca lay in a valley. It was warm, although it was at

an altitude of more than 8,000 feet. It was crowded with people and houses; the valley was green with plants under cultivation. The center of Cajamarca was different from most Inca cities, with a walled plaza. The Inca road that came in from the north entered through a narrow gate where guards were posted. The plaza itself was 500 feet square, with twelve-foot-high walls on three sides. At the west side were a row of houses, royal quarters built of stone. These houses were so close together they were almost like a wall and were to serve as lodgings for the Spaniards. Behind them were other houses and a little farther back was a large outcrop of rock, which towered 300 feet above the plaza. On top of it was a small fortress. At the southern end of the plaza the Inca road continued through another narrow gateway also protected by guards. The road—the same royal Inca road that led to Cusco—led down into the valley, across a bridge over a small river, and on to the hot springs five miles away where the Inca had his headquarters.

That very same evening Pizarro's brother Hernando and Hernando De Soto rode out toward the springs to meet Atahualpa. Fifteen mounted knights went with them, as well as Felipillo, the interpreter. The Spaniards could see steam rising from the springs long before they arrived. It was natural hot water bubbling up from some underground volcano. The Incas' stone baths were beautifully built. Cold water was piped into one side of the bath, natural hot sulphur water into the other. It was as beautiful, said De Soto, as anything the Romans ever had. Some distance away, the Inca waited. Atahualpa sat on a golden stool under an awning. Warriors stood in line on both sides of him, their copper-tipped lances stuck into the ground. It was the first time that Atahualpa had ever seen white men. Still, he showed no surprise. Felipillo took his place at the Inca's side to interpret what the Spaniards had to say. Hernando Pizarro saluted the Inca from his horse. De Soto dismounted, and being a gentleman and knowing how kings should be treated, he made a courtly gesture. He bent his knee and swept the ground with his white plumed hat. Atahualpa liked this, for it was the way that nobles greeted him, with a bow and the caress of a feather.

While De Soto stood at his side, Hernando Pizarro told the Inca of their business. They were retainers of a powerful prince who lived across distant waters. They had heard of his recent great victories and had come to offer him, the Inca, their own services. And also to tell him of the one true God. So they had come to invite the Inca to meet their own Captain-General, Francisco Pizarro. There was other talk, too, of the Pope and his divine powers and his rights to give and take land. This was translated poorly enough by Felipillo. The Inca was displeased with the forwardness of this Indian boy who had been taken to Spain, and he also was displeased with what he knew of the way they had treated his people. Atahualpa answered, "I am greater than any prince on earth. Your emperor may be a great prince; I do not doubt it when I see that he has sent his subjects so far across the waters; and I am willing to hold him as a brother. As for the Pope of whom you speak, he must be crazy to talk of giving away countries which do not belong to him. For my faith, I will not change it."

When Hernando De Soto saw that things were not going well, he changed the subject and asked Atahualpa to honor them with a visit. Then, seeing that the Inca's eyes were on his horse, he quickly mounted. He rode slowly backward for one hundred paces, then spurred. Between the lines of warriors he sped, sending them sprawling. When he was only four paces away from the Inca, he reined the horse up tight. It stood on its rear legs, so close to the Inca that foam from the horse's mouth fell on the royal tunic. Many of the people who surrounded him screamed and ran, but the Inca remained unmoved. And he remembered those who ran. That night he put to death all the chieftains who had dared to show fear.

The Inca accepted the invitation of the Spaniards. As suggested, he would come with no more than five thousand men. His men would come in peace as the Spaniards had, and they would be unarmed so as not to offend their prince.

That night the Spaniards held a council of war. The gunner, Pedro de Candia, and eight men moved his small cannon up to the fortress under cover of darkness. They took with them shot and powder. By morning they had the small, heavy cannon mounted and pointed directly at the center of the plaza.

The Spanish soldiers looked at the thousands of fires burning before the Indians' tents. There were so many that they looked like stars in the sky. Forty thousand warriors against 167 men; 5 million Indians against 167 Spaniards. And there was no way out. No way to return.

Late in the afternoon of the following day, the Inca arrived. The royal procession entered the plaza by way of the narrow south gate. Warriors went ahead, singing their victory songs. Some swept the ground clean so that no dirt might touch the royal Inca. All of them were differently dressed, some in white, others in red; "like squares on a chessboard," remembered one frightened Spaniard watching them approach. The Inca's litter was surrounded by men, all wearing the large golden ear spools that marked them as nobles. The wooden litter was plated with heavy gold leaf etched with patterns of puma and condor heads, and covered with richly woven cloth lined with a mosaic of bird feathers. Atahualpa wore the royal fringe on his head and about his neck hung a massive necklace of engraved gold alternating with huge uncut emeralds.

He and his retinue poured through the narrow doorway and fanned out into the large square of Cajamarca. To his surprise, he found it empty. The Inca waited. There was no one there. He looked around. Everything was quiet, as if the strangers had departed. He spoke to the man beside him.

"Where are the bearded ones?"

"They must be hiding," said the chieftain, "because they are afraid of you."

At that moment, out of the center doorway came a solitary figure, dressed in a heavy white monk's robe. On his chest was an embroidered red cross, symbol of the Order of Mercy. His hair was shorn on top, cut away into a tonsure. He carried a small black book in his hand. As he walked up to where the blue-clad Rucana litter-bearers held the Inca aloft, he was joined by Felipillo, the interpreter. The monk was Vicente de Valverde. By Spanish custom, monks had been sent to win over the Indians' souls. The Spaniard must first of all attempt to bring the Indians into the church, for it was not alone conquest of new lands that the king wanted, nor gold only, although that too was welcome. Their mission was to save the souls of people to whom the Christian God was unknown. Father Valverde was fulfilling the law.

Atahualpa had expected to be met by their leader and to be feted with drink. Instead, he heard a flood of words. There was one God, who was three. There was also a Pope, who had power over all the peoples of the earth.

Atahualpa knew that there were other gods and that every tribe had different names for them. But he knew that his god was supreme. When he heard that someone had power over everyone on earth, he angrily said: "Who says this, and who has the authority to say this?"

Father Valverde handed him his breviary. Atahualpa had never seen a book and could not read. It meant nothing to him. Leafing hurriedly through it and seeing nothing, he grew full of anger. He threw the breviary on the ground.

Pizarro saw this action. By prearranged signals he tossed his white handkerchief into the air. Those Spaniards who were stationed on the fortress overlooking the plaza then fired their cannon. A huge stone cannonball, roaring like thunder, crashed into the thickly packed mass. Then from behind the houses, the soldiers poured out. Those on horses charged into the masses, swinging their swords left and right. Others covered the exits so the Indians could not escape.

"Santiago—and charge!" They shouted an old battle cry. Horses knocked people down and ground them into the earth with their hoofs; soldiers fired into the tightly packed mass. It was all so sudden that the Indians were terrified by the shock of sound and fury. Under the impact many of them fell back against the wall, and under the pressure of bodies the wall collapsed, killing many.

There were a few fortunate ones who were pushed clear. One of these was Huamán.

But what could he or the others do except watch with horror as their Inca was set upon?

Atahualpa's litter was tossed about as if it floated on the open sea. He had to hold on to both its sides to avoid falling out. The litter-bearers fought with the Spaniards even while trying to hold the litter. The Inca's nobles grabbed at the swords with bare hands.

Pizarro then fought his way to the litter.

"Let no one who values his life strike at the Inca," he cried, throwing up his hand just in time to receive a sword stroke

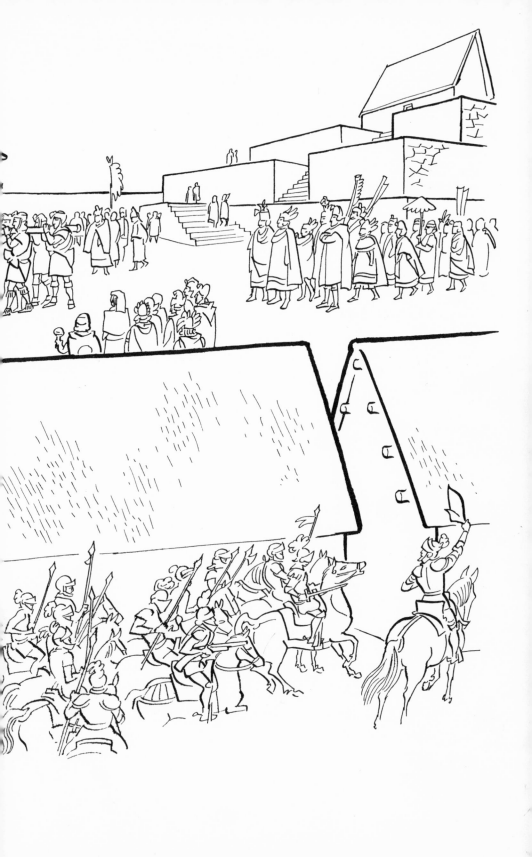

aimed at Atahualpa. It was a slight wound, in fact, the only wound inflicted on the Spaniards during the entire scuffle.

Pizarro seized the Inca. Others dragged him from the litter and quickly bound his arms with ropes, his feet with chains. Everything happened quickly. Three thousand dead and dying lay in the plaza. And all of this happened in thirty-three minutes. In those thirty-three minutes not only the Incas died. A whole series of cultures died with them. The Incas had built their civilization on that of others, those who had come before them. Some of these cultures stretched back farther than 3000 B.C. It had been a slow growth, and the Incas were the heirs to all of it. So it was not alone that the Incas perished; every culture they had succeeded went with them. It all came abruptly to an end.

Atahualpa was now a prisoner. They left him his servants to wait upon him, and he was allowed to talk to some of his nobles. He urged everyone to be calm. After all, he had been a prisoner before and he had escaped. The Spaniards still had to get out of the country, and they were five hundred miles from their ships. Easily sensing the Spaniards' interest in gold, two days after his capture he offered to ransom himself. He told them that if they would release him, he would fill the room where he was captive with gold. He stood up on tiptoe and reached as high as he could. A soldier marked the line with red paint. The room was 17 feet by 22; the mark nine feet from the floor. The conquerors wanted more. Atahualpa also agreed to fill the adjoining room twice with silver plate and ornaments. All this he would do in two months.

Within days the parade of objects, the ransom gold, began. Every day saw the arrival of llamas loaded down with gold. It came from the earth; it came from within the Andes; gold plate was ripped off in large sheets from the buildings in Cusco. The

gold of the Golden Enclosure—golden llamas, corn, and all that
the Indian goldsmiths had made—was brought to Cajamarca.

In all this everyone seemed to have forgotten Huáscar, that
is, everyone except the royal prisoner. Atahualpa worried that
the Spaniards might find that deposed Inca and use Huáscar
against him. But Huáscar's end came very soon. When some
Spaniards passed through Andamarca where Huáscar was being
held captive, he was overheard telling their interpreter that if
they released him, he could provide twice as much gold and
silver as Atahualpa. The very next night, when this information
came to him, even though he himself was captive and many miles
from Andamarca, the imprisoned Atahualpa ordered the execu-

tion of Huáscar. He was strangled and his body thrown into the river.

By February, 1533, Atahualpa had fulfilled his promise. One room was filled with gold plate, the other twice with silver. Pizarro had the king's notary announce it. A soldier blew a trumpet and then, in Spanish, the notary read aloud to the Indians (who could not, of course, understand a word of it) that the Inca had fulfilled his ransom.

Now came the time to melt down the gold. The Inca goldsmiths who had made all these wonderful objects now had to break them up and melt them down into silver and gold ingots. It had to be done this way in order to transport it, and also to pay a certain share to each soldier who had taken part in the conquest and ransom. It was true that the conquistadores thirsted for glory and gold, yet many of them had feelings for the things that they were destroying. Some of the golden objects were just too beautiful to be melted down, so more than a hundred items were set aside. These were sent to Spain to show to the king. It was determined that the gold alone came to a value of 20 million dollars; the silver to over 8 million dollars. It was one of the greatest ransoms ever paid in history for one who eventually failed to secure his freedom.

For it was soon obvious to all that Atahualpa would not leave his prison alive. He loudly demanded it, but Pizarro accused him of plotting against the Spaniards and said that he was secretly raising armies. This was later proved untrue, but now the Spanish feared for their lives. Before, most of them had had nothing to lose but their lives; now, all were rich with ransom gold, so they had the wherewithal to stay alive. Their lives suddenly became precious. They demanded the Inca's head. It was not that easy, however. The king of Spain had sent his own officers with the expedition. They would have to keep to the law. So it was agreed that Atahualpa should be legally tried for his crimes.

Many Spaniards objected to this. Some of them, led by Hernando De Soto, said that they would defend the Inca. They thought that only a king could try a king, and that Atahualpa should be tried in Spain. This was of course quite impossible. So in the end it came out as it had been planned in the first place. Atahualpa was found guilty and was sentenced to be burned at the stake.

When Atahualpa, shackled in chains, was brought the news, his voice lifted up in anger:

"What have I done, or my children, that I should meet such a fate?" Then he turned to Pizarro, saying, "And from your hands, too, you, who have met with friendship and kindness from my people."

Pizarro, it is said, turned away from this speech with tears in his eyes.

On the twenty-ninth of August, 1533, the Inca was led out to his execution. There in the center of the plaza of Cajamarca where he had been captured was a tall wooden stake festooned with chains. About it was wood piled high and ready to be set on fire. Burned at the stake! The Indians knew many terrible forms of death—skinning alive, eyes pulled out, heads broken with stones—and here was still another.

Atahualpa pleaded for his life. Valverde, who attended him, said that if the Inca would allow himself to be baptized, the monk would promise to see that Atahualpa should die by strangulation, a less violent death than burning. Convincing himself that Pizarro would see that this promise was kept, Atahualpa allowed himself to be baptized and declared himself a Christian. He was given the name of Juan de Atahualpa to honor John the Baptist.

Atahualpa was then led to a smaller stake and pushed down on a crude wooden chair. A Spaniard quickly threw a leather thong around his neck and into the loop placed a stick which was twisted until the Inca was garroted to death.

The death of Atahualpa did not mean that the conquest was over. The Spaniards had to fight many a battle; still, the resistance was unorganized. Soon the Spaniards occupied Cusco and made it their mountain capital. They founded Lima on the coast, and a seaport, Callao; and things went well for two years. Then there was an uprising in 1536 led by Manco Inca II, another son of Huayna Capac. Many Spaniards were killed, but in the end they triumphed. Still the Incas kept up their resistance. They continued to fight until 1571. Tupac Amaru, who styled himself "Inca," was captured and beheaded in the plaza at Cusco. Nor was it really the last battle. In 1780 there was another revolt among the Indians, headed by a direct descendant of the Incas, who called himself Tupac Amaru II. The revolt was so serious that it affected much of South America, but within a year he was defeated and he and his followers were, in the manner of the times, drawn and quartered. And that, in 1781, was the final end.

However, the curtain really dropped on the great drama of all these people the night that Atahualpa died.

The Incas: People of the Sun *is a story of the Inca Empire and its subsequent fall as seen through the eyes of Huamán. Huamán is a literary invention, but all the details of daily living are true. They come from reports left by archaeologists, conquistadors, padres, Spanish documents, and from the author's ten-year residence in Peru.*

The part about Alonso de Molina and Ginés, left in Peru in 1527, is also true up to a certain point. These two men belonged to the original thirteen who stayed with Pizarro and who first saw Peru. What happened to them after they were left behind no one knows. The version presented here is what I think could have happened. There are many other versions.

All other events described in the book are history. The dialogues come directly from official Spanish reports of their conquest of Peru. The words spoken by the Inca and the story of his life were told to the Viceroy of Peru twenty years after the conquest, when he spoke to Inca chieftains who remembered what they had seen and heard. This will be found in History of the Incas *by Pedro Sarmiento de Gamboa (written in 1572 and translated into English in 1905) Hakluyt Society, Ser. 2, Vol. 22, 1907. The first reports on the conquest can be read in translation as* Reports of the Discovery of Peru *(written in 1532–1533) Hakluyt Society, No. 47, 1872. A very important book set down in 1532 by a conquistador named Diego de Trujillo has recently been found and published:* Relación del Descubrimiento del Reyno del Perú *(edited by Dr. Raul Porras Barrenechea, Seville, 1948). From these sources and others I have selected the quotations appearing in this book.*

VICTOR W. VON HAGEN

Silvania House, La Molina
Lima, Peru
February, 1961

	INCA WORLD	MEXICO AND CENTRAL AMERICA
B.C.		
	Peruvian Indian cultures begin to develop from farming settlements, about 1200	First farmers arrive at Guatemala, Chiapas, and Yucatán, 2000
A.D. **100–1100**		Rise of Maya civilization, about 350 B.C.–A.D. 300
		Maya culture spreads: period of prosperity, 300–700; building of great stone cities; stone time-markers Tulum, 433
		Kukulkan (Plumed Serpent God) proclaimed ruler and god of Mayas: achieves unity and peace, 987–1017
1100–1200	Manco Capac (1st Inca) founds Cusco, 1150: Beginning of Inca Empire	Aztec migration begins, 1168; settle at Chapultepec
1300–1400	Roca (8th Inca) Beginning of expansion beyond Cusco	Tenochtitlán founded in Lake Texcoco, 1325
	Huaca-chaca suspension bridge across Apurimac, 1350	
1400–1500	Inca power at low point; Chancas sack Cusco, 1438 Incas under Pachacuti defeat Chancas Pachacuti (9th Inca), 1438–1461: Great advancement of Inca civilization Revision of laws to protect Indians; equalization of work-taxes Great period of road building and land development: Cusco rebuilt Road across Andes to coast, completed 1450 Huaca-chaca remade; 3 other bridges across Apurimac Inca territory extends from Lake Titicaca to Lake Chincha Topa (10th Inca), 1461–1493: Continuation of Inca advancement Sacsahuamán fortress built Cajamarca defeated, 1461: Inca influence north to Quito *Chasqui* system introduced Chimús defeated at Chan-Chan, 1466: Incas control coastal area north to Tumpiz Expansion into Chile: Southern boundary fixed at Maule	Aztec civilization at height Mayapán destroyed, 1441: warfare among tribal states (decline of Maya civilization)
1500–1600	Huayna Capac (11th Inca), 1493–1527 Empire reaches maximum extent: 5 million Indians under Inca rule First Inca encounter with Spaniards, 1525; 1527 Huáscar (12th Inca), 1527–1532 Civil war, 1529–1532: Atahualpa defeats Huáscar Spaniards return to Tumpiz, May 1532 Atahualpa (13th Inca), 1532–1533 Spaniards under Pizarro defeat Incas at Cajamarca, Nov., 1532: Execution of Atahualpa marks end of Inca Empire and all preceding Indian civilizations	Spanish explore and conquer Caribbean and northern South America First white men reach Maya coast, 1511 Cortés conquers Mexico, 1519–1521; end of Aztec civilization Spanish conquest of Mayas, 1527–1546

	NORTH AMERICA	EUROPE	NEAR EAST AND ASIA
B.C.			First farmers arrive at Indus valley, about 4000; beginning of Indian civilization about 2100–1300
		Early Minoan Age in Crete	City-state civilizations develop from farming settlements in Tigris-Euphrates valley (Sumeria) and Nile Valley (Egypt), about 3500
			Chinese civilization begins, about 2700
			Buddha, about 560–487
		Alexander the Great conquers Near East; crosses Indus River, 326	
			Unification of Chinese Empire: Great Wall built, 246–210 B.C.
A.D. 100–1100		Roman Empire founded, 27 B.C.	
		Roman Empire at greatest extent, 116	
		Final division into Eastern Roman Empire (Byzantium) and Western Roman Empire (Rome), 395	
		Visigoths sack Rome, 410	
		First great advancement of Byzantine civilization	
		Beginning of modern Western European civilization, 500–600	Tang Dynasty in China; great flowering of Chinese culture
			Beginning of Arab Empire, 632; Arabs conquer Persia, Egypt, North Africa, Spain
		Charles Martel defeats Moslems at Tours, France, 732; stops Arab expansion into Europe	
	Eric the Red discovers Greenland, about 985	Charlemagne crowned emperor of Holy Roman Empire at Rome, 800	
	Leif Ericson visits Vinland, about 1000	William the Conqueror invades England, 1066	
		Crusades against Moslems in Holy Lands, 1096–1270	
1100–1200		Magna Charta in England, 1215	Genghis Khan conquers central Asia and China, 1206–1221; Mongols overthrow Arab Empire, 1258
			Ottoman Empire (Turks) founded, 1288
		Marco Polo visits southern India, 1288, 1293	
1300–1400			Sultanate of Delhi (center of Moslem rule in India), 1206–1526
		Ottoman Turks invade Europe, 1389	
			Tamerlane ruler of Asia, 1369–1405
1400–1500		Renaissance	
		Invention of printing, 1439	Ottoman Turks overthrow Byzantine Empire (1453) and most of Asia; block trade routes to Far East
		Moors expelled from Spain: Beginning of Spanish explorations in New World	
	Columbus discovers America, 1492		
		Vasco da Gama reaches India, 1498	
1500–1600		Magellan voyages around the world, 1519–1522	
			First significant European contact with China
			Beginning of Moghul Empire in India, 1526
		Turkish expansion into Europe stopped at Vienna, 1529	
		Reign of Elizabeth I in England, 1558–1603	
		Defeat of Spanish Armada, 1588; England gains control of seas	
	Pilgrims land at Plymouth, 1620		

BOOKS FOR FURTHER READING

Bird, Junius, and Bennett, Wendell, *Andean Culture History*. New York, American Museum of Natural History Handbook Series No. 15, 1949.

Clark, Ann Nolan, *Secret of the Andes*. New York, The Viking Press, Inc., 1952.

Clissold, Stephen, *Conquistador: The Life of Don Pedro Sarmiento de Gamboa*. London, D. Verschoyle, 1954.

Duvoisin, Roger, *The Four Corners of the World*. New York, Alfred A. Knopf, Inc., 1948.

Lothrop, Samuel Kirkland, *Inca Treasure as Depicted by Spanish Historians*. Los Angeles, The Southwest Museum, 1938.

Mason, J. Alden, *The Ancient Civilizations of Peru*. Baltimore, Penguin Books, Inc., (Pelican Books A395), 1957.

Means, Philip Ainsworth, *Tupak of the Incas*. New York, Charles Scribner's Sons, 1942.

Pigault-Lebrun, Charles A. G., *Theodore, or the Peruvians*. New York, G. Champley, 1825.

Prescott, William H., *The Conquest of Peru*, Victor W. von Hagen, ed. New York, New American Library (Mentor edition MD314), 1961.

von Hagen, Victor W., *Highway of the Sun*. New York, Duell, Sloan & Pearce, Inc., 1955.

———, *The Realm of the Incas*. New York, New American Library (Mentor edition MD192), 1957.

INDEX

ABOUT THE AUTHOR

VICTOR W. VON HAGEN'S expeditions in Mexico and Yucatán, most of the countries of Central and South America, the Galapagos Islands, and the West Indies have made him a recognized authority on the great Indian cultures of this hemisphere.

Mr. von Hagen is the author of more than thirty books, including *Maya. Land of the Turkey and the Deer* and *The Sun Kingdom of the Aztecs,* both for young people. *The Incas* completes his trilogy on the major cultures of the Western Hemisphere before the coming of the white man. When he is not exploring a remote corner of the world—his most recent expedition retraced the route of the famous highway of the Incas throughout Peru and Ecuador—he lives with his wife and family in Lima, Peru.

ABOUT THE ARTIST

ALBERTO BELTRÁN is a young Mexican artist whose artistic abilities and understanding of the ancient Indian cultures of his native land have already earned him a reputation as "the successor to the late Miguel Covarrubias." To illustrate *The Incas: People of the Sun,* Mr. Beltrán visited Peru to gather distinct impressions of the land and the people. He is known in this country for his fine work in *Maya* and *The Sun Kingdom of the Aztecs.*